To Ian

With best wishes for a happy birthday.

from Aunt Mamie

& Uncle Archie.

Opposite: *The new aircraft-carrier H.M.S. Eagle, specially drawn for* EAGLE ANNUAL

THE THIRD

EAGLE

ANNUAL

EDITED BY

MARCUS MORRIS

HULTON PRESS LTD LONDON

John Worsley

The Third · Eagle Annual

CONTENTS

Flame Hits the Trail

A COMPLETE STORY BY ERIC LEYLAND
Illustrated by Alexander Oliphant

"SURE, Scarron is the name, I'm what we call in the States a private eye . . . I think you guys in England call it a private detective. Here are my credentials."

The hatchet-faced American handed papers across the table to David Flame, head of the firm which if it had a name might have been called Adventurers Unlimited.

While David glanced through the papers, Scarron's keen eyes passed from him, lean, brown and at twenty-eight the undisputed boss of the firm, to Ginger Johnston, years older than David, thickset, dour and red of hair . . . and finally to young Tony Carstairs, who was only nineteen.

David handed back the papers. As an adventurer whose main occupation it was to fight the ungodly, he

had heard about the American firm of *Investigators Inc.*, well-known in the States. This Scarron was a typical example of their staff – not much would get past him.

"Right . . . and you're looking for Baldy," he said. "What makes you think we can help ?"

Scarron slipped some gum into his mouth before answering.

"Now see here, Mr Flame, I've heard of you and your pals. You've been fighting crooks for a long time, pretty nearly all over the world. Your Foreign Office and what you call the Special Branch uses you quite a bit. No, don't get worried, what I know I keep to myself. I missed you when you were in the States last but we had word at the office what you were doing and we gave a hand though maybe you didn't know that. It was a minor hand . . . but I remembered you when I landed and I remembered from the newspapers you once had a contact with Baldy."

David said nothing for a few moments. It was true that the firm were used by the authorities on missions of delicacy, but always discreetly. They worked as undercover men, usually with Chief Inspector Patterson of the Special Branch. Undercover . . . but it could never be completely that way. Certain people got to know, the word circulated.

It was true, as well, that four years before the firm had been in contact with a crook known as Baldy – surname unrecorded. Baldy, who operated in the States as well as in England, had worked then as aide to a certain gentleman whom the underworld knew as the Parson. The Parson had gone to gaol, but Baldy had given the authorities the slip, hadn't been heard of since.

GINGER and Tony left the talking to David, though their interest was sharp enough. Scarron had phoned and asked for an appointment. It seemed that he wanted Baldy.

"It's like this," said Scarron, when David had murmured something inconclusive, "six months ago a kid was abducted for ransom in the States. He was found in the end but dead. The gang cleared, but there was a lead that Baldy was implicated. The boy's father employed *Investigators Inc.*, to get Baldy. He's a millionaire and doesn't mind what he spends so long as justice is done. Right . . . we got a lead to England. Do you know anything, Mr Flame ? Have you recently had any word that Baldy is back here ?"

David shook his head. He hadn't heard of Baldy in four years, knew nothing likely to help.

"But there's just one point," he added. "It's queer you should come along just now, Scarron. Baldy worked with the Parson – and if Baldy is dangerous the Parson is more dangerous still. He's half mad, but a genius in his way. When we put him away, four years ago, he threatened to gun for us, for Ginger and me, because Tony wasn't in with us then, when he came out. He was released two weeks ago . . . now you say you've had a tip Baldy may be back here. Interesting that, or it could be."

Ginger Johnston shifted his bulk in the easy chair. He remembered the Parson all right, as dangerous a crook as he had ever encountered; and as David had said, half mad. Tony knew nothing of the man but was anxious to learn. Joining up with the firm at the tender age of nineteen, Tony had already seen much adventure. He was a throw-back to the men of other ages . . . life was not worth living to young Tony unless death was ever present to lend it spice.

"The Parson ?" repeated Scarron. "I've never heard of the guy."

"Maybe you will, though. If you ever see a man with a black widow's peak of hair and a scar down his left cheek, watch it. He can give your gangsters points."

Scarron shrugged his shoulders. He was interested far more in Baldy than in the Parson, who could have had no hand in the kidnapping for at the time he had been in Dartmoor.

"I was hoping the long chance would come off and you'd have a lead to Baldy," he said. "Didn't mind my looking you up, I hope ? I have to try everything, and when I remembered you'd had doings with him I had to contact you. Well, I guess I'd better be going. I can do with some dinner."

It was now seven o'clock in the evening and dark outside, for it was winter. Scarron turned to pick up his hat . . . and at that moment, without warning, the lights went out all over the flat, which was on the ground floor of a large block not far from Hyde Park Corner.

Three people in the room automatically tensed. It might be a fuse, probably was, but it might be . . . sabotage. David and Ginger particularly had lived dangerously so long that any deviation from the normal brought to bear their instinct for danger. Periodically certain individuals who had good cause to dislike them attempted, though so far vainly, to liquidate them. Darkness was often considered an essential to any such attempt.

THERE was no real evidence that in this case the sudden darkness was a preliminary to trouble, but the firm were on their toes within a matter of seconds. Tony was not so experienced as the others but he was well trained. He, like his friends, was at this moment remembering that the Parson was out of gaol – and had threatened to gun for David and Ginger. The familiar tingle ran down Tony's spine at the thought, at the possibility of what he called fun and games.

Ginger made for the door, gun in hand. In another moment he had edged open the front door, leading into the main vestibule. This was in pitch darkness and silent. The hall porter was apparently absent.

The others came up behind Ginger. Then from somewhere beyond the lift shaft opposite came the sound of furtive footsteps, almost instantly stopping. Silence reigned again.

Somebody slipped past Ginger, out of the flat and across the vestibule. David's hand gripped Ginger's arm. Nothing was said, there was no time, for there came the sound of scuffling, a sudden exclamation, then a thud and something metallic fell to the stone floor. It all happened incredibly quickly, with no more than seconds elapsing between the opening of the front door and the noise of what sounded like a fight beyond the lift shaft.

DAVID snapped into action. Ginger was present and Tony was behind him . . . that meant that Scarron had crossed the vestibule. Lithely David moved forward, as yet no other resident appearing to enquire why the lights had gone out. Maybe nobody was at home on the ground floor; and probably the lights were still on above.

Passing the lift, David could see better for the rear service door was standing open, letting in a dim light. For a brief second he saw a man's figure outlined in the doorway, unidentifiable. Then the figure had gone.

David grabbed Tony coming up behind him.

"Get after him . . . but don't use your gun. Trail him if you can and report back here."

Tony slid past him and then Ginger's voice came through the darkness.

"Scarron's here . . . he's bought a packet."

David turned along a cross passage and groped his way forward. Here the open service door gave no help and it was pitch dark. But Scarron's voice identified him.

"I'm O.K. but that guy sure packed a punch."

Suddenly there was light, from a torch. Ginger had been wrestling with a faulty switch but had now made contact. The beam revealed Scarron leaning against the passage wall nursing his jaw. It revealed also a gun lying on the floor, a silencer attached to the barrel . . . and a small scrap of paper gleaming white. David bent down and picked up both the gun and the paper.

"Back to the flat," he murmured, "before the porter gets here."

Ensconced in the flat Scarron explained what had happened. Before he started Tony returned with the news that he hadn't even glimpsed his quarry. The man had disappeared into the narrow streets behind the flats before the boy had reached the service door. It couldn't be helped.

Scarron had moved swiftly as he was trained to do, making for the spot from which the furtive footsteps had sounded. He had found his man but had bought a left to the jaw which had put him down. His assailant had dropped his gun, hadn't stopped to pick it up but had escaped. That was the long and short of it.

David nodded in the light of candles which had been lit.

"The Parson came out of gaol a fortnight ago and maybe he was aiming to put his threat into action. He put the lights out and was reckoning on getting us, maybe . . . what do you think, Ginger?"

Ginger was staring at the scrap of paper David had found on the floor.

"Maybe . . . or it could have been Baldy."

"Or a couple of dozen other thugs who've got it in for us," suggested Tony.

Then Scarron broke in.

"Unless there are two guys with scars down their cheeks and widow's peaks gunning for you it was the Parson. You can take that hard."

Ginger grunted, apparently not put out that a dangerous enemy, half mad, had laid for them and could be presumed to try something similar again.

"Have a look at this," he said, pointing to the scrap of paper.

This had evidently been torn off a letter – off the corner containing the address. This was not complete but it was very interesting:

> . . . ansom,
> . . . swick,
> . . . old,
> . . . uffolk.

Scarron gave an exclamation. The lights went on suddenly, proving that the porter had returned and attended to them, but they paid no attention. Scarron was speaking tensely.

"SNAKES, we're on to something . . . the Parson must have dropped this. Listen, I went to Suffolk yesterday. There was a small-time crook in the States who opened his mouth. He said he'd heard Baldy talking about a village called Walberswick, near a town – Southwold was the name. This hoodlum didn't know what Baldy had meant, but I couldn't afford to pass up any trail so I went down. I didn't get anywhere. I made enquiries but nobody knew anything about anyone looking like Baldy. I reckoned it was a dud trail, but not now, no, sir!"

Silently David lit a cigarette. They were on to something. The Parson was after him, as he had promised. Now he was going after the Parson before he got too dangerous or achieved his ambition to liquidate those who had beaten him four years before. With any luck they'd pull a fast one on the Parson.

"Sure, unless he knows he dropped the paper and reckons we found it," pointed out the more cautious Ginger.

The beam revealed Scarron leaning against the passage wall nursing his jaw.

"We'll take that chance. Scarron, you failed at Walberswick, but it ought to be easy with this," tapping the paper. "The first word must be part of the name of a house. We ought to be able to locate it."

The American nodded grimly. The trail was clear ... and where the Parson was Baldy might also be.

"And vice versa," put in Tony. "I take it we move at once? I'll get my toothbrush!"

"What about the cops?" asked Scarron. "Are you aiming to contact them? From what I hear you don't always."

David's answer was brief. This was a purely private affair with neither the welfare of the state or of any private citizen involved. Even the Baldy business was not official for there was insufficient evidence to secure an extradition warrant, as yet, against the man suspected of the kidnapping in America.

"We tackle it on our own ... but what about you, Scarron? Come if you want to, you moved swiftly enough in the black-out to prove you know your stuff and you'll be useful, but there's no certainty we'll find Baldy. The Parson isn't your objective."

"I'm coming if you'll have me. I've packed my rod and I know how to use it."

So it was arranged, and less than half an hour later

David's Bentley was nosing through the London traffic en route for the Suffolk coast. The four were all armed, and in the car were sandwiches and coffee as rations.

"I reckon I hand it to you guys," was Scarron's comment as London was left behind. "I guess I didn't know Englishmen could hustle like this."

"Tally-ho!" murmured Tony from the back seat.

The journey was uneventful. They reached Blythburgh, only a mile or so from the coast village of Walberswick, just before the inns closed, having achieved a very high average speed. Here they halted outside a small hotel, and, tucking the car round the corner of the building where it was partially concealed by a 'phone-box, David led the way into the place – but minus Scarron, who remained in the car. The presence of an American in the bar might well excite interest, as David pointed out. Undue interest was not desired.

After five minutes or so the firm returned to the Bentley. The car was driven away but was parked again in a lonely lane. Here a swift meal was made off the sandwiches. When the coffee was poured out, David gave Scarron the results of their discreet enquiries at the hotel. There was only one house anywhere near ending in ... *ansom*. This was *Transom*, a small place situated on the edge of the extensive common a mile from Walberswick.

"We'll make for it at once," he added, as the thermos flasks were put away. "The betting is we're not expected. I want to nobble the Parson – he's a naughty boy! Getting after us like that – it's a poor show!"

"He won't be there yet," grunted Ginger, "not unless he's moved down from London pretty well as fast as we've come, which isn't likely."

This was true, but he would come, almost certainly.

"We'll have a look round," added David, "and then hide up and wait for him ... unless Baldy is there and we decide to grab him while the going is good. We can't say anything definite yet, we'll have to go by circumstances. We'll have a look-see first and then decide."

They drove on, reaching the huge common which glimmered under the silver moon. Away to their left stretched the wide estuary of the river, the haunt of water fowl.

The Bentley was halted a mile from the house which could just be glimpsed ahead under the moon. Parking under gorse bushes, David and the others stepped from the car. Then suddenly David reeled. One hand went to his head, he swayed, doubled up and then fell heavily to the turf. He moved once but after that lay motionless.

Tony and Ginger went down almost simultaneously. Tony fell heavily but Ginger put up a fight against whatever had brought him to this state. But it was a losing fight. Eventually he fell, too, and lay without moving.

Scarron came quietly round from the other side of the car. He stood for a moment staring down at the unconscious trio. Then his hand went to his mouth and the cry of an owl, thrice repeated, floated across the common in a signal.

In under five minutes two men came silently on the scene. One was slim and dark with a widow's peak of hair and a scar down his cheek. The other was a gross man, entirely, grotesquely bald. Scarron had caught

that you came over from the States just now. You have been invaluable."

"Sure . . . it was clever of you to work it so they came down here where you can deal with them, boss. You won't forget you owe me dough for what I've done, will you? I guess it was tricky work at first, bluffing them."

"I'll not forget the money. Now we take them all aboard the *Dolphin*. She lies up river and nobody is about. When we are away from land we will settle accounts with Mr Flame and his friends."

Steel hands grabbed the Parson by the throat and simultaneously the toe of one shoe hit Baldy under the jaw with the force of a pile-driver.

up with Baldy but he didn't seem very surprised to see him. He nodded to him and then spoke to the other.

"O.K. Parson, it worked like a dream, like I told you over the 'phone while these mugs were in the pub. Flame fell for me being from *Investigators*, the forged papers were O.K., and the whole bunch fell for the tale about you attacking me and the set-up down here. It was easy. They drank the coffee and they'll be out for a long time. I've got their rods."

The Parson drew back his lips.

"So, at last I can settle with Flame," he murmured, staring malevolently at his enemy. "I have spent four years looking forward to this. How fortunate, Malloy,

He moved forward and bent over Flame. Baldy, hitherto silent, followed and peered over his shoulder.

"The rat," growled Baldy, "but he'll be a dead one before long. He slipped up for once did Mr David Flame."

"Because I was too clever for him . . . get hold of his feet."

Baldy reached down . . . and then David Flame came to life. One moment he was apparently unconscious; the next steel hands had come up and grabbed the Parson by the throat. Simultaneously the toe of one shoe hit Baldy under the jaw with the force of a pile-driver. Baldy staggered back and fell, his jaw as it was afterwards discovered, broken. Then David was on his feet and the Parson was writhing in his iron grasp.

Ginger and Tony had come to life at the same moment. Malloy, *alias* Scarron, stood not a chance. Believing that the three were unconscious, the crook was taken utterly off guard. Tony reached him first, hit him once on the jaw and once with a right-cross in the stomach and that was the temporary end of the unhappy Malloy. Thinking himself safe he hadn't even had a gun in his hand – and neither had Baldy or the Parson.

There was no need to go to David's assistance. He had the Parson in a ju-jitsu grip nothing could break. Tony made for the Bentley, opened the rear door and there were the guns Malloy had taken from what he had considered unconscious prisoners.

That was that. Menaced by the guns the Parson was securely bound and thrown into the back of the car. The other two, incapable of any resistance, only half conscious, were treated in the same way. Half an hour later a startled station sergeant at Southwold had delivered to him three prisoners much the worse for wear.

"Naughty boys," explained David blithely, "look after them carefully, sergeant dear! Oh, yes, and if you think we're nuts, phone up Chief Inspector Patterson of the Special Branch. He'll go bail for us – I hope."

Patterson did. More than that he travelled down to Suffolk and there, some hours afterwards, heard the tale of the hectic period recently experienced.

Carefully David recounted what had happened – though he left out certain deductions made from the facts.

"So there you are," he ended. "The Parson used this Malloy, recently over from the States and a stooge of his in the old days I have no doubt – though we'd never come into contact with him – to play games with us, the object being to get us down here where we could be dealt with conveniently. It was clever and based on an excellent judgment of what we'd do in certain circumstances. Only, of course, I rumbled Mr Malloy early in the proceedings."

"How?" asked Patterson with interest.

David didn't answer at once. He went his own way.

"Malloy 'phoned the Parson from the box outside the inn . . . I hoped he would, guessed he would take the chance. Then he drugged the coffee. One sip was enough to put us wise to that, seeing that I'd told Ginger and Tony about Scarron when we were in the pub . . . we were all on guard. The drugged coffee stunt has been tried on us before. We got rid of it in the darkness and not down our throats. Then we bluffed Malloy for a change, Ginger and Tony taking their cue from me. I'd recognised the dope from the taste and knew what symptoms to fake. I hoped we'd get somewhere and we did, as you know. You can put the Parson and his pals away for attempted murder – very nice."

Patterson sighed. He still didn't know how David had got on to Malloy.

"Oh, that, it was easy. He said he'd been attacked by a scar-faced man at the flats – but it was pitch dark in the cross passage and he couldn't have seen a thing. I couldn't – there was no door there. He was lying – why? The answer became pretty obvious, especially when he talked about Walberswick. He wanted to get us there. . . so we went, but suspecting him made it a walk-over. There was also the fact that he knew too much about our previous contact with Baldy. It wasn't reported in the papers, nothing about us ever is. Anyway, I rumbled him."

Tony Carstairs grinned.

"He hit the right trail," he murmured. "A medal shall be struck for a bright boy! He's training on . . . under my tuition!"

MOTHER: "Bobby, just sit down and tell Johnny a story before he goes to bed."
BOBBY: "I can't sit down, Mummy – I've just told Daddy a story!"

DICK: "That embrocation made my leg smart."
HARRY: "Then why don't you use some on your head?"

F-F-FIERCEST S-S-S-SAVAGES ON E-E-EARTH, HE SAID.... AND C-C-CANNIBALS

AH ~ A WHITE MAN .... HOW NICE. I LEARNED TO SPEAK ENGLISH FROM PREVIOUS WHITE VISITORS, BEFORE EATING THEM.

BUT... OH YES... *YOU* ARE SUCH A *SUPERB* SPECIMEN OF WHITE MAN ~ IT WOULD BE A WASTE TO EAT YOU....

GAD ~ YES. GLAD YOU RECOGNISE A REAL PUKKA SAHIB WHEN YOU SEE ONE, CHIEF!

QUITE!! INSTEAD I WILL STUFF YOU AND PRESERVE YOU FOR POSTERITY... IT IS AN ART IN WHICH WE SPECIALISE!

TAKE HIM AWAY AND TELL THE TRIBE TO PREPARE FOR A CEREMONIAL STUFFING THIS EVENING

GOSH! ~ THEY'RE TAKING HIM INTO THAT HUT...

... SO FAR, SO GOOD. IT LOOKS AS THOUGH I'LL GET OVER TO HIM WITHOUT BEING SEEN...

IT'S ALL RIGHT, SIR... KEEP QUIET... IT'S ONLY ME...

I'LL HAVE YOU UN-TIED IN A JIFFY ~ THEN WE MAY BE ABLE TO SLIP AWAY.

BUT A MINUTE LATER....

NO GOOD... IT'S TOO LATE!! THE TRIBE SEEM TO BE COLLECT-ING FOR SOME BIG CEREMONY

TELL YOU WHAT, THOUGH ~ IF YOU COULD DRESS UP IN THIS MASK AND STUFF YOU MIGHT BE ABLE TO PASS OFF AS ONE OF THEM

AND SO...

HERE YOU ARE, SIR ... YOU'LL LOOK MARVELLOUS IN THIS.

WHEN RAILWAYS RACE

The most exciting sidelight of the Iron Horse's history

BY CECIL J. ALLEN, ILLUSTRATED BY WALKDEN FISHER

HAVE you ever been in a race between two trains? In the ordinary course, such a contest can happen only over a section of line where there are four or more tracks, so that two trains can be running in the same direction simultaneously. In such conditions, to drivers with sporting instincts either the sight of a train ahead on a parallel line, or the fact that they are being overhauled by another train, is a challenge that proves quite irresistible. Many and many a time I have been a witness of ding-dong battles of this kind.

The purpose of this article, however, is to recall some of the historic railway races of the past, when serious attempts were being made by railways to beat one another's fastest times over long distances.

The trains concerned were out of sight of one another, sometimes with nearly a hundred miles of country separating them, but they started and finished their journeys in the same cities, and in certain cases in the same stations. Competition for traffic and in prestige lay behind these contests, and some of them were most exciting affairs.

The first such "race", in 1888, had a fairly simple cause. Until then, the fastest trains between London and Scotland had been reserved for first and second class passengers only, but in 1887 the East Coast companies – the Great Northern, the North Eastern and the North British – decided to open the exclusive "Flying Scotsman" to third class passengers also.

In May, 1888, the West Coast companies (the London & North Western and the Caledonian) decided to cut the time of their 10 a.m. from Euston to Edinburgh by a whole hour – from 10 hours to 9 hours.

This was countered by the East Coast companies, who decided that from July 1st the "Flying Scotsman" should make the run in 8½ hours. This was more than the West Coast companies could stand; now the race was definitely "on".

SCHEDULE times by the two routes were slashed until in no more than 17 days, from July 27th to August 13th, the run of the "Scotsman" from Kings Cross to Edinburgh had been cut from 9 to 7¾ hours, and still the engine-crews were gaining time! On the last day of August 1888, the "Flying Scotsman", leaving London at 10 a.m. made its appearance in Edinburgh at just before 5.27 p.m., and as 26½ minutes had been spent over lunch at York station – this was before the days of restaurant cars – and stops also had been made at Grantham and Newcastle, the actual running time was well under 7 hours – 65 years ago!

Then the competitors agreed that honour had been satisfied, and by common agreement the race came to an end, the schedule times of the day trains between London and Edinburgh settling down to something much more humdrum.

Seven years later there came the "Race to Aberdeen", vastly more exciting because the speeds were much higher, the running was through the night, and because for the last 38 miles of the journey, the competitors' two night trains had to run over the same track.

This time the cause was something more substantial, though five years were to elapse before it had its effect in the amazing speed achievements of August, 1895. In 1890 the opening of the massive Forth Bridge had completed the last link in the direct main line of the North British Railway, up the East Coast of Scotland, and with the second Tay Bridge, opened three years before, it became possible considerably to speed up the East Coast trains between King's Cross, Dundee and Aberdeen; their times were now 15 minutes less than those of the rival route.

The competition between the two sides smouldered for five years, waiting for the slightest breeze to fan it into flame. It came when, at very short notice, the West Coast announced an acceleration of their night "sleeper" from Euston to Aberdeen by no more than 15 minutes, from July 1st, 1895.

The happenings of the next seven weeks were almost incredible. Week after week the booked times of the two flyers – the 8 p.m. from Kings Cross and the 8 p.m. from Euston – became shorter and shorter, because of the slashing cuts in their schedules; and the engine-crews, entering into the spirit of the thing, continued to gain more and more time.

The East Coast authorities lost some of the gains they might have made by holding their train so as not to leave the various stops before time; but the West Coast had no such scruples. So far as their competing train was concerned, they finished by scrapping the time-table altogether, letting the drivers run as fast as they dare, and cutting their three stops – Crewe, Carlisle and Perth – to the miminum; a second train was run to pick up any passengers who might reach the stations too late to catch the express itself. Eventually the East Coast did the same.

The West Coast had the longer route – 540 miles – which took them over the high summits of Shap in Westmorland, Beattock in the Scottish Lowlands, and Gleneagles, in the Highlands; but the East 523½-mile Coast route, on the whole, was the harder, with many severe speed restrictions, especially over the section between Edinburgh and Aberdeen.

Also the lightest weight to which the East Coast flyer diminished was 105 tons, whereas the West Coast finished with a mere featherweight of 70 tons – very little more than a couple of main line corridor coaches today. The engines used, of course, were less than half the weight and considerably less than half the power of the biggest modern express engines.

ALL through July and August the tremendous tussle went on. On August the 18th the "Is line clear?" bells for both trains sounded simultaneously in the signalbox at Kinnaber Junction, just north of Montrose, where the West and East Coast lines met, and the Caledonian signalman chivalrously gave the East Coast train the preference. The climax came on the early mornings of August 21st and 22nd.

On the morning of 20th, the West Coast had got through into Aberdeen by 4.58 a.m. next morning the East Coast simply determined to get there first, and did, at 4.40 a.m., only to be beaten the following morning by the West Coast flyer, which streaked northwards from Euston to such purpose as to come to a dead stand in Aberdeen Central Station at 4.32 a.m., 8 hours 32 minutes after leaving Euston at 8 p.m. on the previous evening. That is to say, the 540 miles, with three stops included, had been run in the amazing time of

512 minutes – and this in 1895, 58 years ago!

Probably the most brilliant West Coast time was that made by the little 2-4-0 engine *Hardwicke* – which is still preserved intact at Crewe Works – for she covered the 141 miles from Crewe to Carlisle, including the negotiation of the 915-foot altitude of Shap Summit, in no more than 126 minutes. Another fine performance was that of the Caledonian 4-4-0 which ran the train over the very hilly 89¾ miles from Perth to Aberdeen in 80½ minutes. On the fastest East Coast night North Eastern 4-4-0 No 1620 succeeded in hurrying her train over the 124½ miles from Newcastle to Edinburgh in 114½ minutes, bringing it into Waverley Station 6 hours 19 minutes after the Kings Cross start. With these epic achievements the competitors regarded honour as satisfied, and far slower times between London and Scotland, which then came into force, remained almost completely unaltered (apart from the 1914-1918 war period and immediately after), until 1932. Then at last it was decided to break the agreement, and to begin the acceleration that culminated in 1937 with the appearance of the "Coronation" and "Coronation Scot" streamliners. But more of that later.

EIGHT years passed before another railway speed contest took place; and this time it was the West of England that was concerned; the competitors were the Great Western and the London & South Western Railways.

Transatlantic steamers were just beginning to forsake Liverpool for Southampton, and in order to shorten the journey time to London, some liners were making calls at Plymouth, from which main lines of both companies ran direct to London.

It was therefore agreed that the South Western should bring up those of the passengers who wanted to get to London quickly in this way, and that the Great Western should handle the mails. Once again it was a question as to who could get there first.

From Stonehouse Junction at Plymouth to Waterloo the South Western had very slightly the longer route. First they had to tackle the tremendous climb over Dartmoor, and then to drop down to Exeter, where, curiously enough, the competing trains ran through St. Davids station in opposite directions.

At least, the South Western train did not *run* through, for the Great Western, which owned St. Davids, rather unsportingly exercised its right to stop its competitor here, so that the latter then had to face the very steep climb up into the L.S.W.R. station from a standing start.

Despite this stop, and a second stop, to change engines, at Templecombe, on April 23rd, 1904, the L.S.W.R. achieved the splendid feat of covering the 230 miles of its very difficult road from Plymouth to Waterloo in just under 4 hours 4 minutes. The 4-4-0 locomotives used throughout had a four-coach load of 105 tons only.

But what was done by the South Western pales beside what the Great Western did with the mails. A series of most brilliant runs concluded with the epoch-making effort of May 9th, 1904, when Plymouth was brought within 3 hours 46¾ minutes of Paddington.

Not only did this time include 3¾ minutes standing, but the stop was at Pylle Hill Junction, *Bristol;* that is to say, the journey was over a distance of 246½ miles, 21 miles further than the 225½ miles over which the "Cornish Riviera Express" today makes its 4¼-hour non-stop journey by way of Westbury.

Perhaps the most astounding part of the run was the time of 56 minutes for the 52 miles from Plymouth North Road to Exeter, with its two extremely hard climbs – to Hemerdon and Dainton, the former as steep as 1 in 42 – and its many sharp curves; today the same run is allowed at least 75 minutes.

What attracted the most attention, however, was the way in which the 4-4-0 engine *City of Truro* swept down the incline from Wellington summit towards Taunton. It was claimed, indeed, that for the first time in British history the three-figure line in speed had been reached, with a maximum of just over 102 m.p.h., and this was sufficient to earn a place for *City of Truro* in York Railway Museum; but critical examination of the records shows that the top speed was probably about 96 or 97 m.p.h. Finally, a 4-2-2 "single-driver", named *Duke of Connaught*, whirled four big mail vans up over the 118½ miles from Plymouth to Paddington in 99¾ minutes, averaging 80 m.p.h. for 70 miles on end, over the perfect "speedway" from Swindon. This day's run was the crowning achievement of the racing from Plymouth to London.

The first world war set British railway speed progress back considerably, but by the middle 1920s speeds had been restored generally to what they had been before the war began.

By now, also, far more powerful and efficient locomotives had come into service; and in 1925 this led to an historic contest in which also the Great Western Railway was concerned. Arising out of an announcement by the G.W.R. that their new *Caerphilly Castle*, on show at Wembley Exhibitions in 1924 alongside the much bigger London & North Eastern Pacific *Flying Scotsman*, was "the most powerful locomotive in

G.N.R. Express of 1880 *hauled by one of the famous Stirling 8 foot Single Locomotives.*

Great Britain", the L.N.E.R. challenged the G.W.R. to prove it.

As a result, the L.N.E.R. 4-6-2 *Victor Wild*, of the "Flying Scotsman" type, went over in 1925 to the G.W.R. for a fortnight, to work the "Cornish Riviera Express", between Paddington and Plymouth and the G.W.R. sent *Pendennis Castle* to the L.N.E.R., to work heavy expresses between Kings Cross and Doncaster.

To cut a long and exciting story short, the Western "Castles" were the winners in both speed and in coal consumption, whether the competitors were burning Welsh coal on the Plymouth run or Yorkshire coal on the Doncaster run. As an outcome of the lessons learned, Sir Nigel Gresley of the L.N.E.R. then made certain alterations to his designs, especially in the matter of valve-setting, and eventually produced his wonderful "A4" streamlined Pacifics in 1935, of which more presently. It is only fair to add that when, in 1948, the nationalised British Railways had a big exchange of locomotives between the Regions for test purposes, it was the ex-L.N.E.R. "A4" design that beat the ex-G.W.R. "King" by a handsome margin, even on Western metals, so turning the tables completely.

A race of another kind was now beginning. Until 1923, the credit for making the fastest daily railway run in the British Empire had gone to the North Eastern Railway, who had a train booked to run from Darlington to York, 44.1 miles, in 43 minutes. In 1923 the Great Western, now very speed-conscious, decided to beat this, and so booked an afternoon Cheltenham-London train to cover the 77.3 miles from Swindon to Paddington in 75 minutes every day. This only meant the difference between 61.7 and 61.8 miles an hour, but it gave the G.W.R. the lead. Such was the modest inauguration of what later became widely known as the "Cheltenham Flyer".

By now railway speeds generally were on the move upwards, and the G.W.R. could not hope to retain its title for long with 61.8 m.p.h. only. By the summer of 1929 the timing came down to 70 minutes, and the autumn of 1932 saw a further cut to 65 minutes. This meant that the "Cheltenham Flyer" had to maintain a start-to-stop average of 71.4 m.p.h. from Swindon to Paddington, and for a very short time this put the G.W.R. in possession of the "blue riband" for the fastest daily time-tabled run in the world. As showing what the Western "Castles" really could do when put to it, also, on June 6th, 1932, *Tregenna Castle* ran the "Flyer" up from Swindon to London in 56¾ minutes, keeping up an average speed of 87½ m.p.h. for 70 miles on end – a wonderful performance indeed.

Now the interest shifts from the west to the north. In the grouping of 1923, the five companies that had competed long before in the "races" to Edinburgh and Aberdeen of 1888 and 1895 had now become two single competitors of far greater resources – the London Midland & Scottish and London & North Eastern Railways.

summer over the 392¾ miles between Kings Cross and Edinburgh, the Scottish capital. To make so long a run possible, special corridor tenders were built, so that a second engine-crew might be able to pass through from the train to the engine, in order to take over for the second half of the run.

It is amusing to recall the way in which the L.M.S.R. stole the L.N.E.R. thunder. With the utmost secrecy, on the Friday before the Monday on which the daily

G.W.R. "City of Truro" 4-4-0 locomotive and train – The forerunner of the famous "Cornish Riviera Express."

After their formation, competition simmered for a time, and the agreements of the original companies not to cut the times between London and Scotland still kept the principal trains to their rather humdrum schedule. But for a while the competition took another form – how far each side could run without stopping to take breath, so to speak.

First of all, in the summer of 1927 the L.N.E.R. decided to run the "Flying Scotsman" non-stop over the 268¼ miles between Kings Cross and Newcastle. Not to be outdone, three months later the L.M.S.R. began to run its "Royal Scot" without any stop between Euston and the Scottish border at Carlisle, 299 miles distant. But the L.N.E.R. played its ace in 1928 by booking the "Flying Scotman" to run non-stop throughout the

L.N.E.R. non-stop run was to begin, the rival route divided the down "Royal Scot" into its Glasgow and Edinburgh sections, and ran both without any intermediate stop to their destinations – the former over 401½ miles and the latter over 399¾ miles, so just beating the length of the L.N.E.R. run. This was only a flash in the pan, however, and throughout its history the 392¾-mile East Coast London-Edinburgh journey, before the war by the "Flying Scotsman", and since by the "Capitals Limited", has enjoyed unchallenged supremacy as the longest regular non-stop run in the world. It is made, however, during the height of the summer season only, whereas the West Coast Euston-Carlisle non-stop is made all the year round, and by several trains daily.

At last, in 1932, there came the end of the agreement not to cut the times between London and Scotland, that had continued since the "Race to Aberdeen" of 1895, and acceleration began. It was cautious at first, and both railways kept more or less in step until the non-stop "Flying Scotsman" of the East Coast and the one-stop "Royal Scot" of the West Coast had both been cut in time from 8¼ to 7 hours on their runs.

Meantime, however, some other very exciting de-

were beating every previous record with a sustained speed that never went below 81 m.p.h. Only 2½ minutes more than two hours took us through Doncaster, 156 miles from London, and in almost exactly 2 hours 32 minutes from Kings Cross we were at rest in the Central Station at Leeds, 185¾ miles away – the shortest time to or from Leeds that had ever been known. Coming back the same afternoon, *Flying Scotsman* was saddled with a couple more coaches, making six in all,

"Mallard", the world's fastest steam locomotive as it appeared in 1938 *when it gained the record of* 126 *m.p.h. for Britain.*

velopments had taken place. Towards the end of 1934 the L.N.E.R. authorities were turning over in their minds how best to mark the Silver Jubilee of the reign of King George V and Queen Mary, which was to be celebrated in the following year. Something very fast and very luxurious in the train realm seemed to be indicated; so two unusual speed trials were planned.

First of all, Leeds was the objective. One murky morning in November, 1934, the famous Pacific *Flying Scotsman*, with her equally famous driver Bill Sparshatt, stole out of Kings Cross with four coaches for a journey which, to those of us in the train, was to prove an amazing experience indeed.

Uphill or downhill, it made little difference to our flying steed; up the long climb to Stoke Summit we

but even so out time up to London was only 5¼ minutes longer, and we had the great satisfaction of touching exactly 100 m.p.h. when descending Stoke bank towards Peterborough.

Less than three months later, another racing trial was staged, this time to and from Newcastle, and again with six coaches. This time the engine chosen was the Pacific *Papyrus*, which not merely made the 268¼-mile run between Kings Cross and Newcastle non-stop in both directions on the same day within an overall compass of 10½ hours, but even gained time on the four-hour schedule that had been laid down. Our gallant engine that day covered no less than 300 miles at an *average* speed of slightly over 80 m.p.h.; but the crowning achievement was on the up journey, when Driver Sparshatt whipped his steed up to 108 m.p.h. on the racing stretch down from Stoke Summit. The fact that this test had been perfectly satisfactory led to the introduction of Britain's first streamlined train, the "Silver Jubilee", in the autumn of the same year, and for its working Britain's first fully streamlined locomotive, the renowned *Silver Link*, first of Gresley's "A4" Pacific class.

The trial trip of this train, on September 27th, 1935 – three days before it was due to begin regular running – was destined to be one of the most thrilling railway runs ever made in Great Britain. Shortly after lunch on this autumn afternoon this unprecedented vision of silver grey and stainless steel made its way out of Kings Cross terminus. Exactly 30 miles out of London the speed crossed the three-figure line; through Hitchin we swept at 107 m.p.h.; soon afterwards we were doing 112½. Indeed, for 25 miles right off the speed was unvaryingly between 100 and 112½ m.p.h., and for 43 miles an average of 100 was maintained – the fastest run of its length in British history. It was a wonderful *première* for the new train. Exactly eleven months later, *Silver Fox*, of the same type, working the up "Silver Jubilee", touched 113 m.p.h. on the descent from Stoke Summit – and while the passengers were having lunch, if you please!

AND what were the rival L.M.S.R. authorities doing all this time? Well, they were certainly wanting to get some of the limelight back, and they got their chance two years later, when the Coronation of King George VI and Queen Elizabeth called for some special commemoration. Both the great competitors decided to celebrate this event by putting into service new streamline trains between England and Scotland, the L.M.S.R. the "Coronation Scot" between Euston and Glasgow, and the L.N.E.R. the "Coronation" between Kings Cross and Edinburgh. It was at the trial trip of the "Coronation Scot", in June, 1937, that the L.M.S.R. determined to get back the blue riband – and did!

The only suitable place for such a speed exploit was the 10-mile descent from Whitmore towards Crewe, the destination of the outward run. So Driver Clarke worked his locomotive *Coronation* to the schedule times laid down until Stafford had been passed, and then he let fly. Speed mounted steadily up the long rise beyond Stafford, and then very rapidly after Whitmore summit had been passed, until at last we got up to 114 m.p.h. – one mile more than the L.N.E.R. record, but enough to claim a victory! It has only to be added that in search of this record the engine-crew left the slowing up for Crewe – now less than 2 miles away – a little too late, and as we bucketted at far too high a speed over the cross-over roads into the platform it was both a mercy and, indeed, a miracle that *Coronation* decided to stick to the rails. But it was a near thing!

To my mind the more remarkable feat that day was the way in which *Coronation* brought the test train back from Crewe to Euston, covering the 158 miles in a minute less than two hours, and keeping up an average speed of 83.3 m.p.h. for 150 miles. The L.N.E.R. had a test run of their new "Coronation" train the same week, and were very disappointed that their engine *Dominion of Canada* did not get quite to 110 m.p.h., so that for a time the L.M.S.R. were the winners. But not for long. For a year only, in fact, because in the summer of 1938 the locomotive authorities decided to stage a record that the L.M.S.R. would be unable to beat, their intentions were concealed under the guise of brake trials, in which a new type of quick-acting brake was being tested, and in particular its efficiency in bringing a train quickly to a stop from the highest speeds.

Thus it was that, on a Sunday in July, 1938, the streamlined locomotive *Mallard* achieved immortal fame. With a train of seven coaches, and Driver Duddington, a man of fearless temperament, at the regulator the test train set out southwards from Grantham. Such a terrific effort did *Mallard* put out that in the 5-mile climb to Stoke Summit all but 75 m.p.h. was reached; then, with almost incredible swiftness, she accelerated until 3 miles later speed had reached 100 m.p.h., 7 miles later 120 m.p.h., and 10 miles later the enormous speed of 126 m.p.h. – the highest fully authenticated speed ever attained in any part of the world with steam locomotion. For five miles *Mallard* travelled at two miles a minute; then the brakes were applied for a curve, and the record was at an end.

So my story comes to an end also, for nothing else of the kind has happened in Great Britain since. Soon afterwards the war brought all high speed to an abrupt conclusion; and since the war not only has British railway speed failed as yet to recover to its pre-war level, but the formation of one nationalised system – British Railways – has put an end to competition also. To those of us who were privileged to take part in these memorable contests, they were exciting beyond measure while they lasted, and remain as unforgettable memories.

DAN DARE
PILOT OF THE FUTURE

Off duty at the Interplanetary Space Fleet Headquarters Dan Dare settles down to catch up with his correspondence. He is interested in a letter from his housemaster, now Head of his old school.

IN

THE DOUBLE HEADED EAGLE

THE OLD PLACE HASN'T CHANGED MUCH.

ALASTAIR, THIS IS DIGBY.

WONDERFUL SHOW YOU BEING HERE, UNCLE. THE HEAD ASKED ME TO TAKE YOU STRAIGHT TO HIM.

CUT ALONG, DARE, AND GOOD LUCK.

WHAT'S SIR HUBERT DOING HERE?

STOLE A MARCH ON YOU, DAN! I'M PRESENTING THE PRIZES AND FROM WHAT I HEAR THE BIG POTS WILL GO TO ALASTAIR

OH, MAGNIFICENT... GOOD BOY... IT'S A NEW RECORD!

YOUR NEPHEW HAS BEEN HONOURED, DAN. HE'S BEEN CHOSEN TO CARRY THE OLYMPIC TORCH ON THE LAST LAP.

THE TORCH? YOU MEAN FOR THE FIRST INTERPLANETARY OLYMPIAD ON VENUS?

THAT EVENING, AFTER THE SCHOOL SPORTS, DAN AND SIR HUBERT ARE ENTERTAINED TO DINNER BY THE HEADMASTER

THAT'S IT, DAN. WOULD YOU LIKE TO FERRY HIM THERE?

GOSH! WOULD I!

25

ON A REGULAR RUN TO VENUS, DAN AND DIGBY COME TO SEE THE WORK IN PROGRESS

HOW ARE THEY GOING TO FIX THE HANDICAPPING, SIR?

IT'LL ALL BE WORKED OUT IN RELATION TO THE GRAVITY OPERATING ON THE CONTESTANT'S OWN PLANETS AND THE GRAVITY OF VENUS

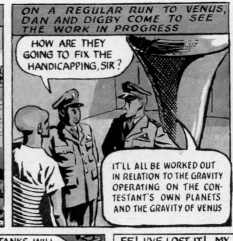

WOULD YOU TAKE MY DOUBLE-HEADED MERCURIAN COIN, SIR? IT WOULD BE BETTER THAN A RABBIT'S FOOT AS A MASCOT FOR YOUNG MR. DARE.

ONE OF THOSE EAGLE COINS, EH? SAME ON BOTH SIDES, TOO. NEVER SEEN ONE LIKE THAT. YOU HANG ON TO IT, ALASTAIR ISN'T SUPERSTITIOUS

IT'S THE ONLY ONE THERE IS

LIKE TO SEE INSIDE THE PLINTH BEFORE WE SEAL IT.

THANKS, SONDAR, WE'LL BE RIGHT WITH YOU.

THESE FUEL TANKS WILL SUPPLY THE OLYMPIC FLAME FOR THE DURATION OF THE GAMES.

SO THAT'S WHAT'S UNDER THE PLINTH.

EE! I'VE LOST IT! MY DOUBLE-HEADED EAGLE! I MUST HAVE DROPPED IT DOWN YON HOLE

WELL, IF IT'S INSIDE THE PLINTH YOU'VE HAD IT! THEY'RE JUST SEALING IT.

STOP WORRYING ABOUT YOUR LOST MASCOT, DIG. WE'LL BE ON EARTH IN TWELVE MINUTES TIME.

'APPEN I'LL GET IT BACK WHEN T'GAMES ARE OVER.

A MONTH LATER THE OLYMPIC TORCH, KINDLED FROM THE SACRED FLAME ON MOUNT OLYMPUS IN GREECE, STARTS ON ITS LONG RELAY VOYAGE WHICH WILL EVENTUALLY BRING IT TO THE OLYMPIC STADIUM ON VENUS....

..... AND AFTER BEING CARRIED ACROSS EUROPE IS TAKEN INTO THE SPACESHIP JUNO FOR THE LAST LAP, TO VENUS

DANGER
SPACE SHIP
TAKING OFF
DO NOT PASS
THIS POINT

DURING THE JOURNEY TO VENUS THE TORCH IS PLACED IN AN OXYGEN FED CONTAINER.

WE'LL BE IN GOOD TIME. I'M LANDING ON THE OLD DISUSED AIRFIELD. YOU'LL SLEEP OUTSIDE MEKONTA AND TO-MORROW RUN WITH THE TORCH TO THE OPENING OF THE STADIUM. NERVOUS?

I'M SO EXCITED I SHAN'T BE ABLE TO SLEEP, UNCLE.

TELL THE COLONEL I WILL MEET HIM. I HAVE GRAVE NEWS.

RIGHTO, SONDAR, OVER AND OUT.

IN THE CONTROL ROOM AT THE OLD DISUSED AIRPORT NEAR MEKONTA

EE! WHATEVER'S TO DO?

I HAVE DISTURBING NEWS, COLONEL. ONE OF OUR TREEN MECHANICS HAS JUST DIED AFTER AN ACCIDENT... BEFORE...

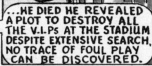

...HE DIED HE REVEALED A PLOT TO DESTROY ALL THE V.I.Ps AT THE STADIUM DESPITE EXTENSIVE SEARCH, NO TRACE OF FOUL PLAY CAN BE DISCOVERED.

IT'S FANTASTIC. DO YOU BELIEVE IT?

WE MUST INVESTIGATE, O COLONEL — WE CANNOT TAKE ANY CHANCES.

THE CHAP WAS PROBABLY DELIRIOUS. THE GAMES CAN'T BE STOPPED WITHOUT CAUSE.

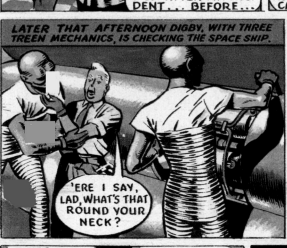

LATER THAT AFTERNOON DIGBY, WITH THREE TREEN MECHANICS, IS CHECKING THE SPACE SHIP.

'ERE I SAY, LAD, WHAT'S THAT ROUND YOUR NECK?

EE! IT'S MY DOUBLE-HEADED EAGLE!

YOURS?. NO! — ER — IT WAS GIVEN TO ME BY MACCA, OUR CHAMPION OLYMPIC RUNNER...

MACCA WAS ONE OF THE MEKON'S HIGHEST LIEUTENANTS BUT HE IS SUPPOSED TO HAVE BEEN CONVERTED.

WHAT ON VENUS...?

SORRY, SIR, BUT JUST LOOK AT THIS!

DON'T YOU SEE, SIR. I DROPPED THIS INT'H' PLINTH JUST BEFORE IT WAS SEALED. SOMEBODY'S BEEN INSIDE IT SINCE! THIS MACCA CHAP MUST KNOW SOMETHING. HOW DID HE GET IT?

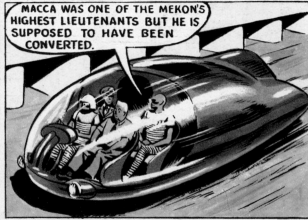

NO, O SONDAR, MACCA IS NOT HERE. HE HAS BEEN EXCUSED THE OPENING PARADE BECAUSE HIS FATHER IS ILL IN THE COUNTRY.

HE IS AT THIS ADDRESS. IT IS A SMALL FARM IN THE ATLANTINE COUNTRY. IT IS A LONG WAY AWAY.

I MUST QUESTION HIM AT ONCE. LEND ME A ROTOR JEEP.

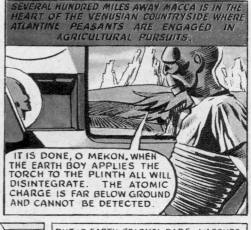

SEVERAL HUNDRED MILES AWAY MACCA IS IN THE HEART OF THE VENUSIAN COUNTRYSIDE WHERE ATLANTINE PEASANTS ARE ENGAGED IN AGRICULTURAL PURSUITS.

IT IS DONE, O MEKON. WHEN THE EARTH BOY APPLIES THE TORCH TO THE PLINTH ALL WILL DISINTEGRATE. THE ATOMIC CHARGE IS FAR BELOW GROUND AND CANNOT BE DETECTED.

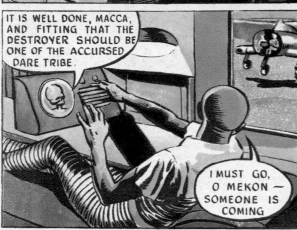

IT IS WELL DONE, MACCA, AND FITTING THAT THE DESTROYER SHOULD BE ONE OF THE ACCURSED DARE TRIBE.

I MUST GO, O MEKON — SOMEONE IS COMING

HI, THERE! SHOW A LEG! I WANT TO ASK YOU A FEW QUESTIONS.

BUT, O EARTH COLONEL DARE, I ASSURE YOU AN ADMIRER GAVE ME THE COIN AS A MASCOT. I CANNOT EVEN REMEMBER WHO IT WAS.

HE'S LYING

IT'S NOT IMPORTANT. I REALLY CAME TO TELL YOU TO RETURN WITH ME

WHY? I CANNOT UNDERSTAND

THE COMMITTEE HAVE DECIDED TO HONOUR YOU. YOU ARE TO CARRY THE TORCH INTO THE ARENA AND LIGHT THE FLAME ON THE PLINTH WITH IT.

ME? . . . . PLINTH? . . . NO . . . I CANNOT . . . I MUST DECLINE . . . . MY FATHER . . . .

WHY, YOU . . .

HELLO! THERE'S SOMETHING IN HIS HOLSTER —

PHEW! YOU'RE RIGHT, DIGBY — IT'S A BOMB. AN ATOMIC BOMB UNDER THE PLINTH AND BY THE LOOK OF IT, IT WILL GO OFF WHEN ALASTAIR *LIGHTS THE FLAME WITH HIS TORCH*

LOOK OUT, SIR!

TIE HIM UP, DIG! . . . WE MUST GET TO MEKONTA IMMEDIATELY. THAT BOMB WILL BLOW UP THOUSANDS OF THE MOST IMPORTANT PEOPLE IN THE INNER PLANETS.

BUT AS DAN AND DIG RACE THEIR MACHINE AWAY FROM MACCA'S HOUSE AN ATLANTINE TRACTOR IS EMERGING FROM A STORAGE BARN

I'LL TRY TO GET SIR HUBERT ON THE RADIO.

CRASH

AFTER HIS ACCIDENT DAN SLEEPS HEAVILY FOR 8 HOURS IN THE HOME OF ONE OF THE ATLANTINE FARMERS

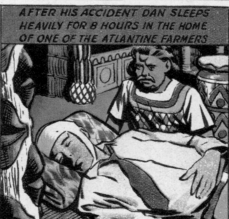

GOSH! IT'S ONLY AN HOUR TO ZERO HOUR!

IT IS FORTUNATE, COLONEL DARE. THAT I KNOW YOUR LANGUAGE. I AM A BROTHER OF THE DAPON.

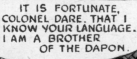

THERE ARE NO TRANSMITTERS IN THIS SETTLEMENT, NOR ANY FAST METHOD OF TRANS- PORT, BUT I CAN LEND YOU A FORAGE FREIGHT

DAN AND DIG MAKE FOR THE NEAREST TREEN POST.

QUICK! LET ME USE YOUR TELEVIEWER. I MUST GET SIR HUBERT GUEST AT THE OLYMPIC STADIUM

BUT, O COLONEL, IT IS TOO LATE. WE CANNOT RADIO THE STADIUM. THERE IS A RAY BARRIER TO PREVENT TRANSMISSION OF THE SPORTS RESULTS EXCEPT THROUGH THE INTERPLANETARY NEWS SERVICE AND IT HAS ALREADY STARTED.

TAKE THIS. IT IS AN ATOMIC SPRAY MACHINE FOR THE ORCHARDS . BUT REMEMBER YOU CANNOT LAND WITHIN THE OUTER PERIMETER OF THE STADIUM BECAUSE OF THE RAY BARRIER.

OH, COME ON, OLD JALOPY, WE'VE GOT TO MAKE IT!

10 MINUTES BEFORE THE OPENING OF THE GAMES

I CAN'T UNDERSTAND WHY DAN HASN'T REPORTED

WELL, WE'D BETTER BE GETTING IN OUR PLACES, SIR HUBERT.

ALASTAIR WILL BE NEARING THE STADIUM — I CAN HEAR CHEERING IN THE DISTANCE!

WHAT A MAGNIFICENT SIGHT! — MAKES ME FEEL AS YOUNG AS YOU, PROFESSOR!

THIS IS BETTER THAN THE CUP FINAL. I WISH DAN WERE HERE TO SEE HIS NEPHEW!

HERE'S ALASTAIR NOW — WITH THE TORCH.

BUT WHAT'S HAPPENING BEHIND HIM? — LOOK! IS SOMEBODY GATECRASHING?

IT'S DISGRACEFUL!

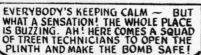

AND SO, THANKS TO DIG'S DOUBLEHEADED EAGLE, THE FIRST INTERPLANETARY OLYMPIAD WAS INAUGURATED — SAFELY.

THIS WAS NOT THE ONLY TIME THAT THE EARTH ANTHEM WAS PLAYED.

ALASTAIR ALONE WON THAT HONOUR TWICE DURING THE MEETING.

BUT THE MOST AMAZING TROPHY WENT TO DIGBY

... AND GOVERNOR SONDAR HAD THIS SPECIALLY MADE FOR YOU, DIGBY.

So, Auntie, as that old double-headed Eagle played such a part in it all I'm sendin' it to you.

....OH MY!!

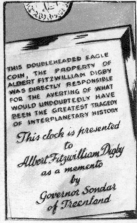

THIS DOUBLEHEADED EAGLE COIN, THE PROPERTY OF ALBERT FITZWILLIAM DIGBY WAS DIRECTLY RESPONSIBLE FOR THE AVERTING OF WHAT WOULD UNDOUBTEDLY HAVE BEEN THE GREATEST TRAGEDY OF INTERPLANETARY HISTORY

This clock is presented to Albert Fitzwilliam Digby as a memento by Governor Sondar of Treenland

Drawn by Donald Harley from a story by John Myers based on characters invented by Frank Hampson.

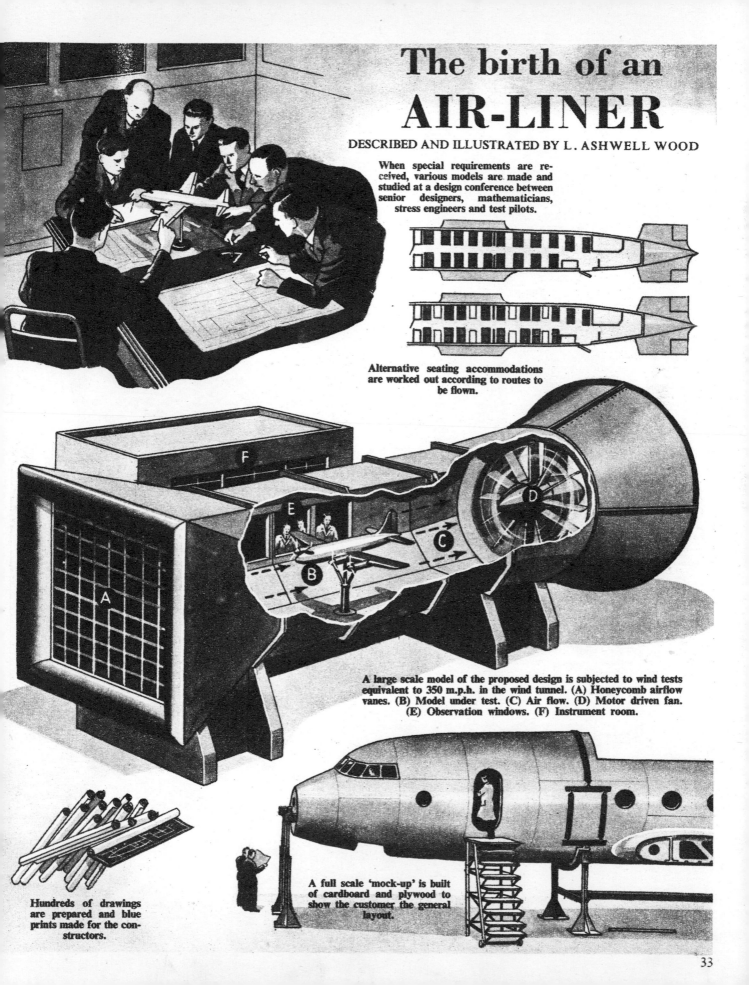

The birth of an AIR-LINER

DESCRIBED AND ILLUSTRATED BY L. ASHWELL WOOD

When special requirements are received, various models are made and studied at a design conference between senior designers, mathematicians, stress engineers and test pilots.

Alternative seating accommodations are worked out according to routes to be flown.

A large scale model of the proposed design is subjected to wind tests equivalent to 350 m.p.h. in the wind tunnel. (A) Honeycomb airflow vanes. (B) Model under test. (C) Air flow. (D) Motor driven fan. (E) Observation windows. (F) Instrument room.

Hundreds of drawings are prepared and blue prints made for the constructors.

A full scale 'mock-up' is built of cardboard and plywood to show the customer the general layout.

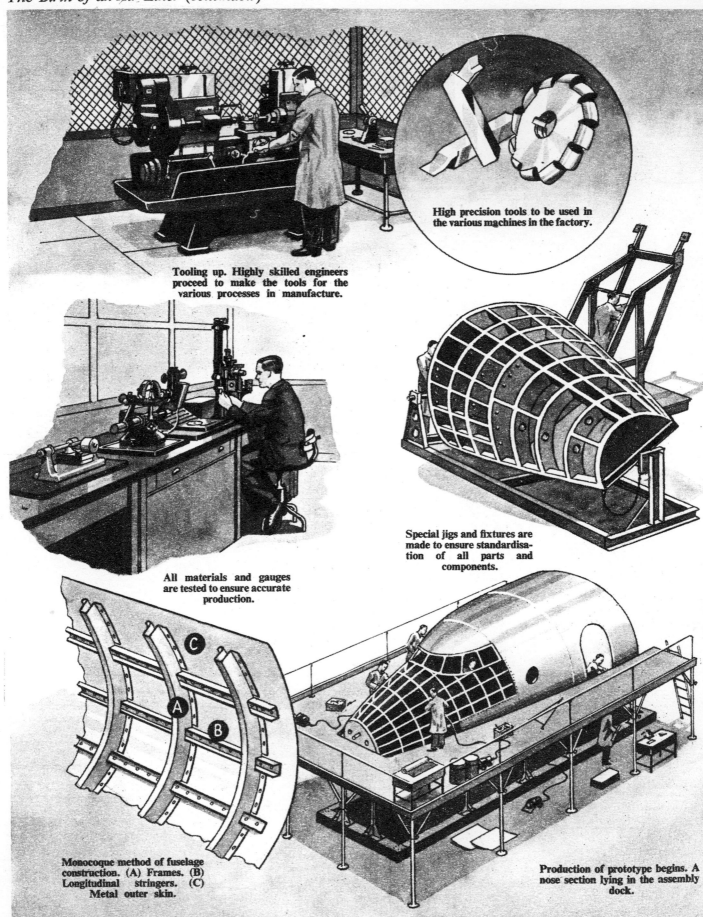

High precision tools to be used in the various machines in the factory.

Tooling up. Highly skilled engineers proceed to make the tools for the various processes in manufacture.

All materials and gauges are tested to ensure accurate production.

Special jigs and fixtures are made to ensure standardisation of all parts and components.

Monocoque method of fuselage construction. (A) Frames. (B) Longitudinal stringers. (C) Metal outer skin.

Production of prototype begins. A nose section lying in the assembly dock.

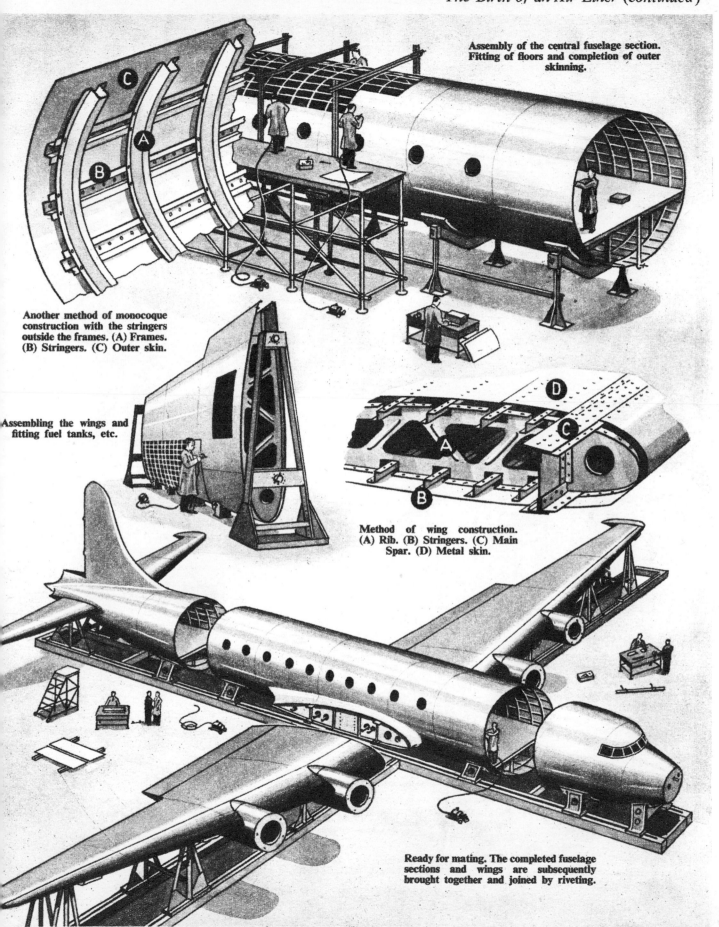

Assembly of the central fuselage section. Fitting of floors and completion of outer skinning.

Another method of monocoque construction with the stringers outside the frames. (A) Frames. (B) Stringers. (C) Outer skin.

Assembling the wings and fitting fuel tanks, etc.

Method of wing construction. (A) Rib. (B) Stringers. (C) Main Spar. (D) Metal skin.

Ready for mating. The completed fuselage sections and wings are subsequently brought together and joined by riveting.

Meanwhile propellers are made and machined. The hub end of a propeller blade on a profile-copying machine.

High-altitude chamber. The aircraft and its detached wings are tested under conditions of low air-pressure and intense cold.

The form of power is decided on and engines ordered from the manufacturers. A jet turbo-prop engine under test.

Final assembly. Fitting engines, propellers, undercarriages, ailerons, rudder, etc.

After gruelling test flights, the aircraft is ready to be handed over to the operating company.

Completed aircraft swung for compass adjustment and weighed.

L. ASHWELL WOOD

P.C.49
IN
THE CASE OF THE
STAR PUPIL
by *Alan Stranks.*
Drawn by *Alfred Sindall.*

SHORTLY BEFORE THE EXAMINATIONS AT THE BLYTHE STREET SCHOOL, CYRIL (GIGLAMPS) FOSTER WAS RETURNING HOME BY UNDERGROUND, WHEN.....

SORRY, GUV'NOR!

CAREFUL MAN! YOU'LL HAVE ME OVER.

HURRY ON PLEASE!

STOP, THIEF!

THIS MAN STOLE YOUR WALLET SIR. I SAW HIM DO IT!

LOOKS LIKE SID'S COPPED. JUST AS WELL HE WAS SLIPPY IN PASSING ME THIS WALLET. I'D BETTER GET AWAY FROM HERE-FAST.

THE KID'S CRAZY! I NEVER PINCHED NOTHINK. GO ON - SEARCH ME!

SOMEBODY *HAS* ROBBED ME! MY WALLET'S GONE!

WE'D BETTER TAKE HIM UPSTAIRS AND REPORT THIS TO THE STATION-MASTER.

AND CALL THE POLICE!

THAT'S ALL I'VE GOT. YOU CAN SEE FOR YOURSELVES THERE'S NO WALLET. THIS KID'S BEEN GOING TO THE PICTURES TOO MUCH.

ARE YOU SURE YOU HAVEN'T MADE A MISTAKE, YOUNG MAN?

HERE COMES JOE NOW WITH A COPPER.

POSITIVE! HE STOLE IT ALL RIGHT, BUT HE'S FOUND SOME WAY OF GETTING RID OF IT.

WE'LL SEE WHAT THE POLICE HAVE TO SAY ABOUT THIS.

HELLO-ELLO! WHAT SEEMS TO BE THE TROUBLE?

FORTYNINE!

CRIKEY! IT WOULD BE *HIM!*

SOMEBODY PICKED MY POCKET AND *HE'S* THE ONE WHO DID IT, FORTYNINE.

I KNOW THIS BOY AND HE'S NO LIAR. IT LOOKS LIKE YOU'RE UP TO YOUR OLD LARKS AGAIN, MR. SID SNITCH.

DON'T LISTEN TO THAT LYING BRAT, COPPER!

THERE WAS OVER FIFTY POUNDS IN THAT WALLET.

YOU'RE MAKING A MISTAKE, COPPER - AND YOU'LL LIVE TO REGRET IT. THAT KID, TOO.

SAVE IT FOR THE MAGISTRATE, SID MY BOY!

HE MUST'VE SLIPPED THE WALLET TO A CONFEDERATE IN THE CROWD.

THE KID'S A ROTTEN LITTLE LIAR.

THE BOY HAS GIVEN HIS EVIDENCE IN A STRAIGHT-FORWARD MANNER. I SEE NO REASON TO DOUBT HIM. SID SNITCH! YOU ARE COMMITTED TO STAND YOUR TRIAL AT THE OLD BAILEY.

SILENCE, YOU!

NEXT MORNING AT THE POLICE COURT...

I NEVER THOUGHT THE 'BEAK' WOULD GRANT HIM BAIL.

DISGRACEFUL! HE'S GOT CROOK WRITTEN ALL OVER HIM.

I SUPPOSE I'LL BE CALLED TO GIVE EVIDENCE AT HIS TRIAL, FORTYNINE?

I'LL HAVE NO CHANCE AT THE OLD BAILEY WITH *MY* RECORD. I'VE *GOT* TO FIX THAT KID SOME WAY.

THERE'S ONLY ONE WITNESS AGAINST ME TWISTER-THAT KID! IF WE CAN FIND SOME WAY OF PROVING HE'S A LIAR, I MIGHT HAVE A CHANCE AT MY TRIAL. I HEARD HIM SAY HE LIVES AT NUMBER TWENTY-SEVEN LAUREL GROVE. WE'LL GO OUT AND 'TAIL' HIM TO SEE WHAT WE CAN FIND OUT ABOUT HIS HABITS.

IT WAS NO GOOD ME HANGING AROUND WHEN THEY 'NICKED' YOU, SID. HERE'S YOUR SHARE.

THAT EVENING -

LATER THAT NIGHT, SID SNITCH AND TWISTER LAWLESS TRAIL GIGLAMPS FOSTER FROM HIS HOME TO THE BOYS' CLUB HEADQUARTERS.

YOU CAN GET A GOOD LOOK AT HIM NOW, TWISTER. IT'S THAT LITTLE MUG WEARING GLASSES.

I SEE HIM!

37

SCENIC BUILDING *for* MODEL RAILWAYS
Written and illustrated by WALKDEN FISHER

Nº 1 TRACKSIDE EMBANKMENTS

THE DEVELOPMENT OF A SCENIC SCHEME IS AN INTERESTING ASPECT OF THE MODEL RAILWAY HOBBY AS EVEN THE SIMPLEST TYPE OF LAY-OUT CAN BE EASILY TRANSFORMED.
THE FEATURES HERE ILLUSTRATED ARE DESIGNED FOR THE SHELF-TYPE OF LAYOUT IN OO GAUGE. BUT WITH A LITTLE INGENUITY SIMILAR IDEAS MAY BE USED IN A TABLE-TOP LAYOUT, AND FOR O GAUGE.

THE PACKING-PAPER METHOD OF FORMING EMBANKMENTS AND ROCK-CUTS IS SIMPLE AND INEXPENSIVE. CRUMPLE A SHEET INTO A BALL, UNCRUMPLE IT AND GLUE INTO POSITION ALONG TOP EDGE OF CUT-OUT BANKING SHAPE Ⓐ AND ALONG BASE BOARD AT POINT Ⓑ.

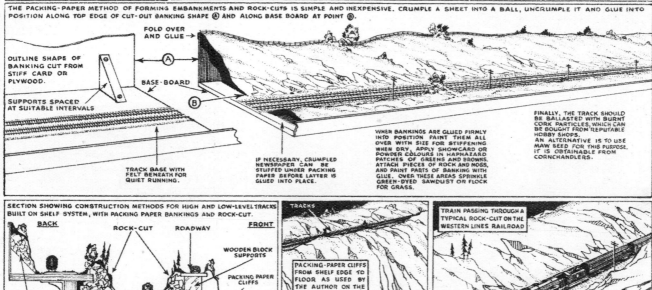

FOLD OVER AND GLUE →

OUTLINE SHAPE OF BANKING CUT FROM STIFF CARD OR PLYWOOD.

SUPPORTS SPACED AT SUITABLE INTERVALS

BASE-BOARD

TRACK BASE WITH FELT BENEATH FOR QUIET RUNNING.

IF NECESSARY, CRUMPLED NEWSPAPER CAN BE STUFFED UNDER PACKING PAPER BEFORE LATTER IS GLUED INTO PLACE.

WHEN BANKINGS ARE GLUED FIRMLY INTO POSITION PAINT THEM ALL OVER WITH SIZE FOR STIFFENING. WHEN DRY, APPLY SHOWCARD OR POWDER COLOURS IN HAPHAZARD PATCHES OF GREENS AND BROWNS. ATTACH PIECES OF ROCK AND MOSS, AND PAINT PARTS OF BANKING WITH GLUE. OVER THESE AREAS SPRINKLE GREEN-DYED SAWDUST OR FLOCK FOR GRASS.

FINALLY, THE TRACK SHOULD BE BALLASTED WITH BURNT CORK PARTICLES, WHICH CAN BE BOUGHT FROM REPUTABLE HOBBY SHOPS.
AN ALTERNATIVE IS TO USE MAW SEED FOR THIS PURPOSE. IT IS OBTAINABLE FROM CORNCHANDLERS.

SECTION SHOWING CONSTRUCTION METHODS FOR HIGH AND LOW-LEVEL TRACKS BUILT ON SHELF SYSTEM, WITH PACKING PAPER BANKINGS AND ROCK-CUT.

BACK / ROCK-CUT / ROADWAY / FRONT
WOODEN BLOCK SUPPORTS
PACKING PAPER CLIFFS
CRUMPLED NEWSPAPER
CRUMPLED NEWSPAPER

TRACKS
PACKING-PAPER CLIFFS FROM SHELF EDGE TO FLOOR AS USED BY THE AUTHOR ON THE 'WESTERN LINES' MODEL RAILROAD, A STANDARD OO GAUGE LAYOUT.
GUARD BOARD TO PREVENT DAMAGE

TRAIN PASSING THROUGH A TYPICAL ROCK-CUT ON THE WESTERN LINES RAILROAD

Nº 2 MAKING MODEL TREES

TREES GREATLY INCREASE THE REALISM OF SCENIC LAYOUTS, AND HERE ARE SOME IDEAS AND METHODS WHEREBY AT LITTLE COST, MODEL TREES THAT WILL BE VERY LIFE-LIKE IN APPEARANCE MAY BE MADE IF CARE AND PATIENCE IS USED!

CUT SOME LENGTHS OF SOFT WIRE ABOUT HALF AS LONG AGAIN AS HEIGHT TREE IS TO BE. CLAMP THEM IN A VICE IN A BUNCH ABOUT AN INCH FROM ONE END.

WITH A PAIR OF PLIERS TWIST THEM TOGETHER UNTIL POINT IS REACHED WHERE IT IS DECIDED TO START FIRST BRANCHES. SELECT SEVERAL WIRES FROM MAIN BUNCH AND TWIST AWAY SEPARATELY FROM TRUNK. BEND AND KINK THEM AT THE SAME TIME.

MAIN BUSH OF WIRES FORMING TRUNK

GO ON UNTIL ALL WIRES ARE TWISTED AND BENT TO SHAPE ALL ROUND TRUNK. NEXT WRAP STRIPS OF THIN PAPER AROUND TRUNK, MOULDING IT OVER WIRES AND PASTE WELL.

THIN PAPER STRIPS AROUND TRUNK

PAINT WHOLE TREE WITH THIN GLUE AND SPRINKLE WITH BROWN FLOCK POWDER.

TOUCH UP TRUNK AND BRANCHES WITH VARIOUS SHADES OF GREEN, BROWN AND YELLOW POSTER COLOURS.
FOR FOLIAGE, FOAMED RUBBER OR SPONGE CAN BE PLUCKED TO SHAPE AND PUSHED ON TO BRANCHES COATED WITH GLUE.
WHEN SET: SPRAY FOLIAGE WITH SHELLAC VARNISH USING A MOUTH SPRAY. TOUCH UP WITH MATT OIL COLOURS.

BASEBOARD
DRILL HOLE IN BASEBOARD. TWIST WIRES AT BASE OF TRUNK AND INSERT. FIX WITH GLUE.
BIND AND PASTE THIN PAPER STRIPS ROUND TRUNK BASE TO MASK HOLE. PAINT TO MATCH TRUNK.

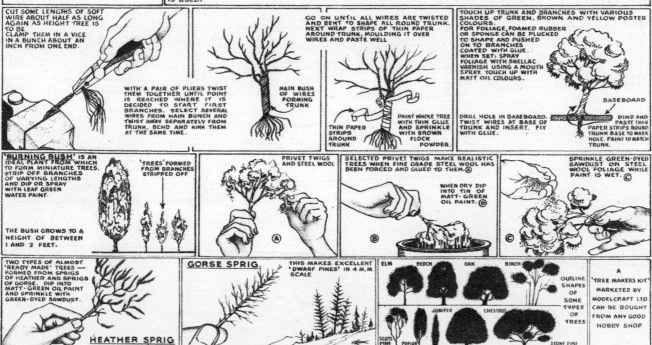

'BURNING BUSH' IS AN IDEAL PLANT FROM WHICH TO FORM MINIATURE TREES. STRIP OFF BRANCHES OF VARYING LENGTHS AND DIP OR SPRAY WITH LEAF GREEN WATER PAINT.
THE BUSH GROWS TO A HEIGHT OF BETWEEN 1 AND 2 FEET.

'TREES' FORMED FROM BRANCHES STRIPPED OFF

PRIVET TWIGS AND STEEL WOOL
SELECTED PRIVET TWIGS MAKE REALISTIC TREES WHEN FINE GRADE STEEL WOOL HAS BEEN FORCED AND GLUED TO THEM. Ⓐ
WHEN DRY DIP INTO TIN OF MATT-GREEN OIL PAINT. Ⓑ
SPRINKLE GREEN-DYED SAWDUST ON STEEL WOOL FOLIAGE WHILE PAINT IS WET. Ⓒ

TWO TYPES OF ALMOST 'READY MADE' TREES — FORMED FROM SPRIGS OF HEATHER AND SPRIGS OF GORSE. DIP INTO MATT-GREEN OIL PAINT AND SPRINKLE WITH GREEN-DYED SAWDUST.
HEATHER SPRIG

GORSE SPRIG
THIS MAKES EXCELLENT 'DWARF PINES' IN 4 M.M. SCALE

ELM / BEECH / OAK / BIRCH
SCOTS PINE / POPLAR / JUNIPER / CHESTNUT / STONE PINE
OUTLINE SHAPES OF SOME TYPES OF TREES

A 'TREE MAKERS KIT' MARKETED BY MODELCRAFT LTD. CAN BE BOUGHT FROM ANY GOOD HOBBY SHOP.

Nº 3 MODELLING A TUNNEL PORTAL

THIS TYPE OF PORTAL IS FOR A SINGLE-TRACK TUNNEL. A DOUBLE-TRACK PORTAL CAN BE MADE IN SIMILAR MANNER.
YOU ARE RECOMMENDED TO STUDY EXAMPLES OF REAL TUNNELS FOR ARCHITECTURAL DETAILS.

FROM A PIECE OF WOOD Ⓐ WITH A MINIMUM THICKNESS OF 1 INCH, CUT OUT THE TUNNEL MOUTH SHAPE Ⓑ DECIDED UPON, WITH A FRET-SAW.

MAKE SURE THAT THE CUT IS VERTICAL ALL ROUND THE SHAPE

MINIMUM OF 1 INCH

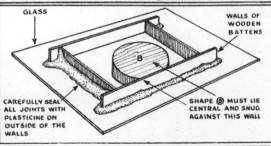

GLASS

WALLS OF WOODEN BATTENS

CAREFULLY SEAL ALL JOINTS WITH PLASTICINE ON OUTSIDE OF THE WALLS

SHAPE Ⓑ MUST LIE CENTRAL AND SNUG AGAINST THIS WALL

PLACE Ⓑ ON A FLAT, LEVEL SURFACE, SUCH AS A PIECE OF GLASS.

BUILD UP FOUR WALLS WITH PIECES OF WOOD BATTENING, OR OTHER SUITABLE TIMBER AS SHOWN.

Ⓑ SHOULD LIE CENTRAL AND SNUG AGAINST O WALL AS ILLUSTRATED.

THE WALLS CAN BE HIGHER THAN THE THICKNESS Ⓑ BUT *NOT LOWER*.

ALL THE INTERIOR SURFACES OF THE WALLS — THE FLOOR OF THE 'BOX', AND THE VERTICAL FAC OF SHAPE Ⓑ SHOULD BE GIVEN A THIN FILM OF FINE OIL. "3 IN ONE" OIL IS EXCELLENT FO THIS.

NEXT, IN A BASIN, MAKE A MIX OF PLASTER OF PARIS AND WATER TO A CONSISTENCY OF THICK CREAM.

NOTE: THOROUGHLY CLEANSE THE BASIN IMMEDIATELY AFTER POURING THE MIX AS THE PLASTER SETS RAPIDLY!

POUR MIX INTO 'BOX' UNTIL IT COMES LEVEL WITH THE TOP OF Ⓑ.

ALLOW TO SET FOR 15 TO 30 MINUTES. THEN REMOVE WALLS AND CAREFULLY EASE OUT SHAPE Ⓑ

WHEN BLOCK IS THOROUGHLY DRIED OUT, BRICKWORK OR MASONRY CAN BE SCRIBED WITH A SHARP POINT ON ITS SURFACE.
OTHER ADDITIONS CAN BE CEMENTED ON.
INTERIOR SHOULD BE PAINTED MATT BLACK, AND EXTERIOR WASHED WITH POSTER PAINTS IN VARYING SHADES OF GREY AND BROWN. THE COLOURS WILL SINK INTO THE SCRIBED LINES GIVING A VERY REALISTIC EFFECT.
HOLD LIGHTED MATCH OR CANDLE IN ARCHWAY AND ALLOW SMOKE TO FORM SOOT STAIN OVER CENTRE.

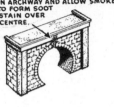

THE TUNNEL PORT IN POSITION

Nº 4 BUILDING RETAINING WALLS AND FENCES

THE FEATURES DEALT WITH HERE ARE SIMPLE TO MAKE. THEY CAN ADD A GREAT DEAL TO THE REALISM OF A MODEL LAYOU

A RETAINING WALL MADE FROM TWO PLYWOOD SHEETS GLUED TOGETHER.

STRIP-WOOD COPING

STRIP-WOOD

ARCHWAYS CUT WITH FRET-SAW FROM OVERLAYING PLY-WOOD SHEET

BACK STRIP FORMING RECESSED WALL OF ARCHWAYS.

COVER WITH BRICK, OR STONE PAPER, ON SALE IN SHEETS FROM MOST MODEL RAILWAY HOBBY SHOPS.

A SIMPLE, STRAIGHTFORWARD VERSION WITH STRIP-WOOD BUTTRESSES. IT CAN BE FINISHED OFF WITH BRICK OR STONE PAPER, OR AS PLAIN CONCRETE. A SEARCH THROUGH THE ADVERTISEMENTS OF ALMOST ANY COLOURED MAGAZINE SHOULD PROVIDE PLENTY OF POSTERS. BEAR IN MIND THE SCALE TO WHICH YOU ARE WORKING AND SELECT SUITABLE PORTIONS OF THE ADVERTS.

Read EAGLE EVERY FRIDAY

STRIP-WOOD BUTTRESSES

PLAN VIEW SHOWING BUTTRESS CAPS AND COPING. MAKE THESE FROM CARD OF SUITABLE THICKNESS.

A RETAINING WA BUILT AROUND ROCKY LEDGE 'ROUGH COUNTR

THIS ILLUSTRATES HOW A RETAINING WALL CAN BE USED TO SAVE SPACE IN A CUTTING.

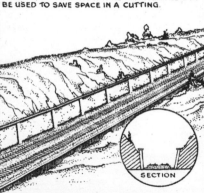

SECTION

THERE ARE MANY WAYS OF CONSTRUCTING FENCES, AND MANY TYPES TO CHOOSE FROM. FINE STRIP-WOOD, AS USED BY AERO-MODELLERS CAN BE WORKED WITH GOOD EFFECT.

SPACE UPRIGHTS NOT MORE THAN 6 SCALE FEET APART.

A POST-AND-WIRE TYPE

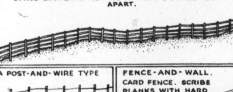

INSERT USED MATCH STICKS INTO HOLES DRILLED IN BASE-BOARD. WIND GREY COTTON THREAD BETWEEN THEM

FENCE-AND-WALL CARD FENCE. SCRIBE PLANKS WITH HARD PENCIL. COLOUR CREOSOTE.

STRIP-WOOD WALL COVERED WITH BRICK PAPER.

STRIP-WOOD CAPPING

MAKE THIS UP ON THE SITE BY SOLDERING LENGTHS OF WIRE TO UPRIGHT PINS SET IN HOLES.

PINS SET IN HOLES DRILLED IN BASEBOARD.

CORRUGATED IRON, IN FOI 4 M.M. SCALE CAN BE BOUC FROM G.N. SLATER & SON MANCHESTER

COLOUR WOODEN POSTS CREOSOTE

MODELCRAFT LTD. HAVE PRODUCED A CARD MODELLIN SHEET OF PLATFORM FENCING IN FULL COLOUR — DESIGNED BY EDWARD BEAL.

IT IS EASILY MADE UP AND VERY EFFECTIVE.

PLATFORM FENCING IN MACHINED CARD-STRIP OR MET IS NOW AVAILABLE AT MOST MODEL RAILWAY HOBBY SHOP

ARTIST'S BRISTOL BOARD IN VARYING THICKNESSES IS AN IDEAL MATERIAL FOR MODEL BUILDINGS. STRAWBOARD SHOULD ONLY BE USED AS A LAST RESOURCE! IF THIS BECOMES NECESSARY, FIRST COAT IT WITH GLUE OR SIZE TO FORM A PRIMING COAT FOR EASIER WORKING. BRICK AND STONE PAPERS FOR O AND OO GAUGE SCALES CAN BE BOUGHT AND WILL HELP GREATLY. A KEEN CUTTING TOOL IS ESSENTIAL, AND ONE OF THE TRIX "X-ACTO" MODELLERS' KNIVES WILL BE FOUND TO BE EXTREMELY USEFUL.

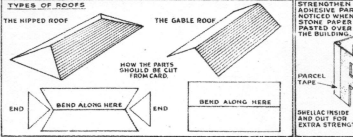

TYPES OF ROOFS

THE HIPPED ROOF — THE GABLE ROOF.

HOW THE PARTS SHOULD BE CUT FROM CARD.

END — BEND ALONG HERE — END

BEND ALONG HERE

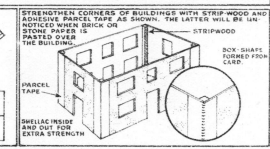

STRENGTHEN CORNERS OF BUILDINGS WITH STRIP-WOOD AND ADHESIVE PARCEL TAPE AS SHOWN. THE LATTER WILL BE UNNOTICED WHEN BRICK OR STONE PAPER IS PASTED OVER THE BUILDING

STRIPWOOD

BOX-SHAPE FORMED FROM CARD.

PARCEL TAPE

SHELLAC INSIDE AND OUT FOR EXTRA STRENGTH

WINDOW OPENINGS. MARK OUT WITH PENCIL AND PIERCE HOLES WITH PIN AT EACH CORNER BEFORE CUTTING

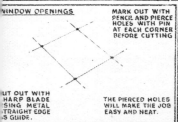

CUT OUT WITH SHARP BLADE USING METAL STRAIGHT EDGE AS GUIDE.

THE PIERCED HOLES WILL MAKE THE JOB EASY AND NEAT.

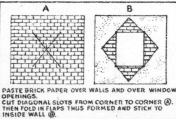

A   B

PASTE BRICK PAPER OVER WALLS AND OVER WINDOW OPENINGS. CUT DIAGONAL SLOTS FROM CORNER TO CORNER (A). THEN FOLD IN FLAPS THUS FORMED AND STICK TO INSIDE WALL (B).

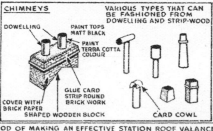

CHIMNEYS

VARIOUS TYPES THAT CAN BE FASHIONED FROM DOWELLING AND STRIP-WOOD

DOWELLING

PAINT TOPS MATT BLACK

PAINT TERRA COTTA COLOUR

GLUE CARD STRIP ROUND BRICK WORK

COVER WITH BRICK PAPER SHAPED WOODEN BLOCK

CARD COWL

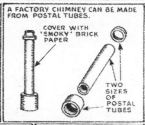

A FACTORY CHIMNEY CAN BE MADE FROM POSTAL TUBES.

COVER WITH "SMOKY" BRICK PAPER

TWO SIZES OF POSTAL TUBES

GUTTERS: A NOVEL METHOD AS SUGGESTED BY EDWARD BEAL.

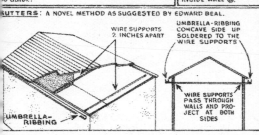

WIRE SUPPORTS 2 INCHES APART

UMBRELLA-RIBBING CONCAVE SIDE UP SOLDERED TO THE WIRE SUPPORTS

WIRE SUPPORTS PASS THROUGH WALLS AND PROJECT AT BOTH SIDES

UMBRELLA-RIBBING

JOHN H. AHEARN'S METHOD OF MAKING AN EFFECTIVE STATION ROOF VALANCE.

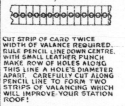

CUT STRIP OF CARD TWICE WIDTH OF VALANCE REQUIRED. RULE PENCIL LINE DOWN CENTRE. WITH SMALL LEATHER PUNCH MAKE ROW OF HOLES ALONG THIS LINE A HOLE'S DIAMETER APART. CAREFULLY CUT ALONG PENCIL LINE TO FORM TWO STRIPS OF VALANCING WHICH WILL IMPROVE YOUR STATION ROOF!

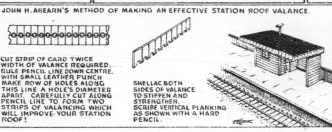

SHELLAC BOTH SIDES OF VALANCE TO STIFFEN AND STRENGTHEN. SCRIBE VERTICAL PLANKING AS SHOWN WITH A HARD PENCIL.

AN EXCELLENT SERIES OF CARD CONSTRUCTIONAL SHEETS ("BILTEEZI SERIES") FOR VARIOUS TYPES OF BUILDINGS IN 4 M.M. SCALE IS AVAILABLE FROM HAMBLINS, 10 CECIL COURT, CHARING CROSS ROAD, LONDON, W.C.2. THE CARDS ARE PRINTED IN FULL COLOUR.

№6 MAKING A REALISTIC LAKE (PART ONE)

THE FEATURE DESCRIBED IN THIS AND THE NEXT SECTION IS INTENDED FOR A PERMANENT LAYOUT. IT CAN PROVE TO BE ONE OF THE CHIEF SCENIC ATTRACTIONS OF A MODEL RAILWAY SYSTEM. THE COST IS VERY SMALL AND NO UNUSUAL SKILL IS NEEDED IN THE BUILDING.

TO MAKE A MODEL LAKE USING REAL WATER IS IMPRACTICAL BECAUSE OF THE DAMPNESS, SMELL OR STAGNATION IT WOULD CAUSE. ALSO IT WOULD HAVE A VERY UNNATURAL RIPPLE-FREE SURFACE UPON WHICH A FILM OF DUST WOULD EVENTUALLY FORM. HAMMERED GLASS IS THE BEST MATERIAL FOR SUCH A FEATURE.

DECIDE UPON SITE AND SIZE OF LAKE, THEN CUT A HOLE, HAVING AN IRREGULAR CONTOUR, OUT OF THE BASE-BOARD.

BASE-BOARD

BASE-BOARD SUPPORTS

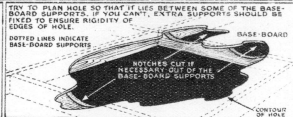

TRY TO PLAN HOLE SO THAT IT LIES BETWEEN SOME OF THE BASE-BOARD SUPPORTS. IF YOU CAN'T, EXTRA SUPPORTS SHOULD BE FIXED TO ENSURE RIGIDITY OF EDGES OF HOLE.

BASE-BOARD

DOTTED LINES INDICATE BASE-BOARD SUPPORTS

NOTCHES CUT IF NECESSARY OUT OF THE BASE-BOARD SUPPORTS

CONTOUR OF HOLE

NEXT, MAKE A 'HANGING BAG' OF FINE CHICKEN NETTING. STAPLE NETTING AROUND OUTLINE AND PRESS AND FASHION IT WITH THE FINGERS INTO HUMPS AND RIDGES TO FORM THE UNEVEN SLOPING CONTOURS OF THE LAKE-BED.

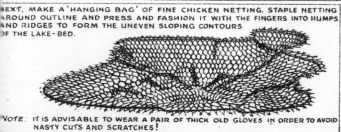

NOTE: IT IS ADVISABLE TO WEAR A PAIR OF THICK OLD GLOVES IN ORDER TO AVOID NASTY CUTS AND SCRATCHES!

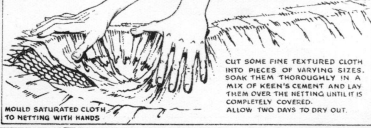

MOULD SATURATED CLOTH TO NETTING WITH HANDS

CUT SOME FINE TEXTURED CLOTH INTO PIECES OF VARYING SIZES. SOAK THEM THOROUGHLY IN A MIX OF KEEN'S CEMENT AND LAY THEM OVER THE NETTING UNTIL IT IS COMPLETELY COVERED. ALLOW TWO DAYS TO DRY OUT.

WHEN CEMENT-SOAKED CLOTH HAS ALMOST DRIED OUT IT IS READY FOR PAINTING. THE FINISHED EFFECT OF THE LAKE DEPENDS A GREAT DEAL ON THIS 'UNDER WATER' PAINTING. APPLY THE COLOURS IN THE ORDER SHOWN IN THE NEXT DIAGRAM. COMMENCING WITH THE DEEPEST PORTIONS OF THE LAKE AND WORKING UP TO THE SHORE LINE. PAINT THE SHADES ON ROUGHLY WITH A RAG. DO NOT MAKE DEFINITE LINES OF COLOURS BUT MERGE ONE INTO THE OTHER WHILE THEY ARE STILL WET. IT DOESN'T MATTER IF SOME RUN DOWN INTO OTHERS. IT ALL ADDS TO THE FINISHED EFFECT!

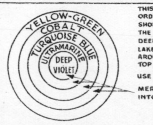

YELLOW-GREEN
COBALT
TURQUOISE BLUE
ULTRAMARINE
DEEP VIOLET

THIS CHART SHOWS THE ORDER IN WHICH COLOURS SHOULD BE APPLIED. THE CENTRE REPRESENTS DEEPEST PORTIONS OF LAKE. WORK UP AND AROUND FROM THIS TO TOP (SHORE-LINE)

USE POSTER PAINTS.

MERGE EACH SHADE INTO NEXT.

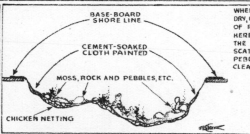

BASE-BOARD SHORE LINE

CEMENT-SOAKED CLOTH PAINTED

MOSS, ROCK AND PEBBLES, ETC.

CHICKEN NETTING

WHEN COLOURS ARE DRY, CEMENT PIECES OF ROCK AND MOSS HERE AND THERE ON THE LAKE-BED, AND SCATTER A FEW PEBBLES AND FINE CLEAN GRIT ABOUT.

DO NOT OVERDO THIS!

№ 7 MAKING A REALISTIC LAKE (PART TWO)

IN THE PRECEDING DIAGRAMS, INSTRUCTIONS FOR CONSTRUCTING AND PAINTING THE BED OF THE MODEL LAKE WERE GIVEN. DETAILS OF HOW TO PUT THE FINISHING TOUCHES TO THE LAKE AND ITS SURROUNDINGS ARE EXPLAINED.

HAVING PAINTED AND ARRANGED ALL THE UNDER-WATER DETAILS, NEXT OBTAIN A SHEET OF "HAMMERED GLASS". THERE ARE VARIOUS TYPES. CHOOSE ONE WITH AN UNEVEN RIPPLE-LIKE SURFACE. ANY GLAZIER SHOULD BE ABLE TO SUPPLY IT, AND THE COST FOR A SHEET 2 OR 3 FEET SQUARE WILL ONLY BE A FEW SHILLINGS. THE GLASS SHOULD BE LARGE ENOUGH TO OVERLAP THE LAKE CAVITY BY A GOOD MARGIN ALL ROUND.

THE MANNER IN WHICH THIS TYPE OF GLASS BREAKS UP AND MERGES THE UNDER-WATER DETAILS, GIVES A MOST REALISTIC EFFECT.

ALLOW A GOOD OVERLAP ALL ROUND THE LAKE CAVITY.

NOW IS THE TIME TO CHECK ALL THE UNDER-WATER DETAILS. MAKE SURE THAT EVERYTHING IS IN PLACE BEFORE LAYING THE GLASS OVER THE CAVITY. NEXT, WITH THE GLASS IN POSITION, ITS OVERLAP IS COVERED BY HEAPING SAND OR FINE GRIT AND SMALL PEBBLES UPON IT TO THE EDGE OF THE CAVITY BENEATH. THIS IS CARRIED OUT ALL ROUND THE LAKE.

HAMMERED GLASS

BASE-BOARD
OVERLAP OF GLASS

ROCKS

SAND, OR FINE GRIT AND PEBBLES HEAPED AND SPREAD OVER GLASS, OVERLAP TO EDGE OF CAVITY.

BACK FROM SHORE SPRINKLE GREEN-DYED SAWDUST TO REPRESENT GRASS.

FORM SHORE OF FINE GRIT OR SAND

SMALL HILLOCKS CAN BE FORMED WITH PACKING PAPER TREATED IN EXACTLY THE SAME MANNER AS DESCRIBED FOR BANKINGS IN № 1 OF THIS SERIES.

BASE-BOARD

HAMMERED GLASS SHEET OVERLAPPING LAKE CAVITY AND RESTING ON BASE-BOARD

BASE-BOARD SUPPORTS

ROCKS, PEBBLES, GRIT AND MOSS GLUED IN POSITION ON LAKE-BED. CHICKEN NETTING COVERED WITH CEMENT-SOAKED CLOTH

MOSS

FIX TREES IN SUITABLE POSITIONS BACK FROM THE SHORE. THE CONSTRUCTION OF VARIOUS TYPES OF MODEL TREES WAS DEALT WITH IN № 2 OF THIS SERIES.

№ 8 A MODEL LOG CABIN IN 4 M.M. SCALE (OO GAUGE)

THIS MODEL CAN MAKE AN ATTRACTIVE FEATURE WHEN PLACED IN THE VICINITY OF THE MODEL LAKE DESCRIBED IN THE TWO PREVIOUS SECTIONS. GENERAL DIMENSIONS ARE GIVEN. HOWEVER, THE MODELLER CAN LET HIS IMAGINATION GO FREE AND USE HIS OWN INGENUITY OVER DESIGN. IT IS SELDOM THAT TWO CABINS ARE IDENTICAL, AND THEREFORE ONLY THE MAIN CONSTRUCTIONAL METHODS FOR SUCH A MODEL ARE EXPLAINED HERE.

START BY COLLECTING A SUPPLY OF USED MATCH STICKS. THESE SHOULD ALL BE OF THE SAME TYPE, MATCHES VARY! OTHER MATERIALS REQUIRED ARE SOME PIECES OF CARD OF SUITABLE THICKNESS, SOME LENGTHS OF STRIPWOOD, PARCEL TAPE, MODEL CEMENT — SECCOTINE OR CROID GLUE. FOR TOOLS SCISSORS AND A SHARP KNIFE SHOULD BE SUFFICIENT. COMMENCE BY MAKING THE FOUR WALLS FROM CARD AND IN THEM CUT DOORS AND WINDOWS TO SUIT YOUR OWN INDIVIDUAL TASTE!

NOTE: DIMENSIONS GIVEN IN FIRST DIAGRAM ARE ONLY INTENDED AS GUIDE. CABIN CAN BE MADE LONGER, WIDER & SLIGHTLY HIGHER IF DESIRED.

STRIPWOOD IN CORNERS

1¼ INS.
1 IN.
1½ INS.
3 INS.

STRENGTHEN CORNERS WITH STRIPWOOD AND ADHESIVE PARCEL TAPE.

COAT INSIDE AND OUT WITH SHELLAC VARNISH

WHEN SHELLAC HAS DRIED AND HARDENED, THE WALLS ARE READY FOR THE 'LOGS' TO BE GLUED ON. SELECT SOME MATCH STICKS, CUT AND TRIM THEM TO REQUIRED LENGTHS AND GLUE UPRIGHT FROM TOP TO BOTTOM ON EACH SIDE OF EVERY WINDOW AND DOOR.

UPRIGHT 'LOGS' GLUED TO CARD WALLS EACH SIDE OF DOOR AND WINDOWS

NEXT, CAREFULLY CUT SOME MATCH-STICKS TO FIT HORIZONTALLY BETWEEN THESE UPRIGHTS, AS SUGGESTED IN THE ILLUSTRATION. DO NOT FIX ANY FROM OUTER UPRIGHTS TO CORNERS YET.

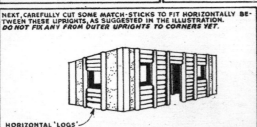

HORIZONTAL 'LOGS'

FOR THE CORNERS EXTRA CARE IS NECESSARY IN CUTTING THE MATCH-STICKS TO FIT. NOTE HOW EACH IS NOTCHED IN ORDER FOR THEM TO FIT ONE ABOVE THE OTHER.

TRIM MATCHES TO FIT SLOPE OF ROOF

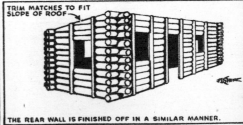

THE REAR WALL IS FINISHED OFF IN A SIMILAR MANNER.

PASTE TRACING PAPER OVER WINDOWS ON INSIDE. A DOOR IS MADE BY GLUEING MATCH-STICKS ON A PIECE OF CARD AS SHOWN. MAKE IT A GOOD FIT AND GLUE INTO POSITION ON THE INSIDE OF THE DOOR OPENING.

FIT SHINGLE ROOF AS ILLUSTRATED, ALLOWING A GOOD OVERHANG BACK AND SIDES. THE CONSIDERABLE OVERHANG AT THE FRONT FORMS ROOF OF BALCONY.

DOWEL PAINTED BLACK

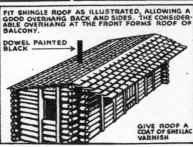

GIVE ROOF A COAT OF SHELLAC VARNISH

ROOF SHINGLES MADE FROM CARD STRIPS CUT AND LAID AS SHOWN

CARD STRIP

CUT SLITS WITH SCISSORS ABOUT ¼ INCH APART

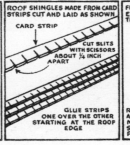

GLUE STRIPS ONE OVER THE OTHER STARTING AT THE ROOF EDGE

FINAL DETAILS: GLUE CABIN ON CARD BASE WHICH SHOULD EXTEND TO FORM FRONT BALCONY FLOOR. RULE PLANKING THIS PORTION WITH A HARD PENCIL.

CARD BASE

ROOF SUPPORTS AND BALCONY RAILS MADE FROM MATCH-STICKS GLUED IN POSITION.

STRIPWOOD SUPPORT RUN WIDTH OF FLOOR

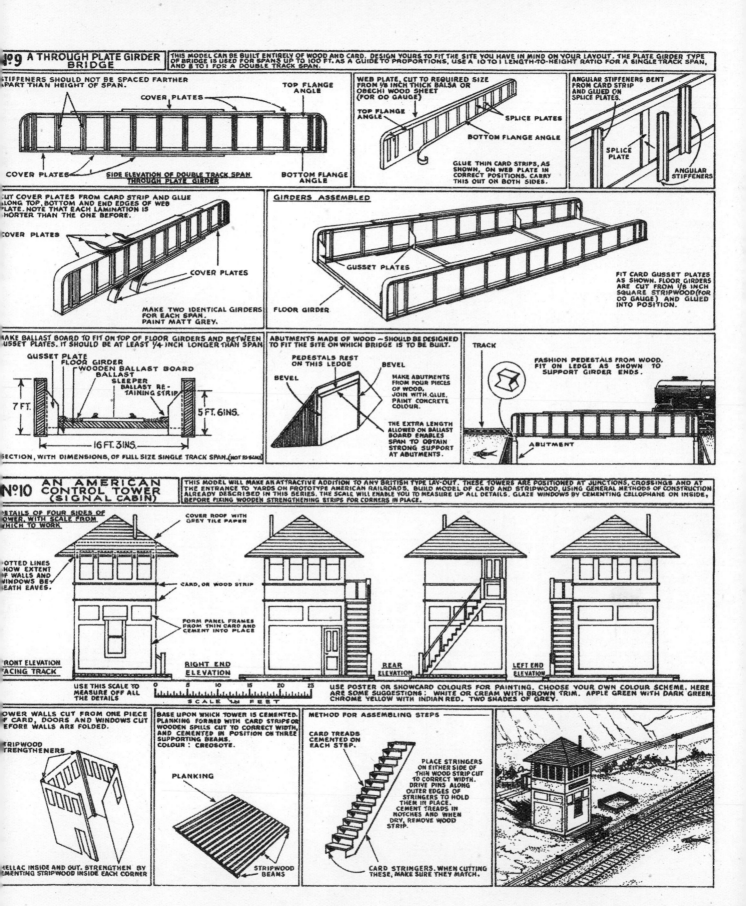

Nº 9 A THROUGH PLATE GIRDER BRIDGE

THIS MODEL CAN BE BUILT ENTIRELY OF WOOD AND CARD. DESIGN YOURS TO FIT THE SITE YOU HAVE IN MIND ON YOUR LAYOUT. THE PLATE GIRDER TYPE OF BRIDGE IS USED FOR SPANS UP TO 100 FT. AS A GUIDE TO PROPORTIONS, USE A 10 TO 1 LENGTH-TO-HEIGHT RATIO FOR A SINGLE TRACK SPAN, AND 8 TO 1 FOR A DOUBLE TRACK SPAN.

STIFFENERS SHOULD NOT BE SPACED FARTHER APART THAN HEIGHT OF SPAN.

COVER PLATES
TOP FLANGE ANGLE
COVER PLATES
BOTTOM FLANGE ANGLE
SIDE ELEVATION OF DOUBLE TRACK SPAN THROUGH PLATE GIRDER

WEB PLATE, CUT TO REQUIRED SIZE FROM 1/8 INCH THICK BALSA OR OBECHI WOOD SHEET (FOR OO GAUGE)
TOP FLANGE ANGLE
SPLICE PLATES
BOTTOM FLANGE ANGLE
GLUE THIN CARD STRIPS, AS SHOWN, ON WEB PLATE IN CORRECT POSITIONS. CARRY THIS OUT ON BOTH SIDES.

ANGULAR STIFFENERS BENT FROM CARD STRIP AND GLUED ON SPLICE PLATES.
SPLICE PLATE
ANGULAR STIFFENERS

CUT COVER PLATES FROM CARD STRIP AND GLUE ALONG TOP, BOTTOM AND END EDGES OF WEB PLATE. NOTE THAT EACH LAMINATION IS SHORTER THAN THE ONE BEFORE.
COVER PLATES
COVER PLATES
MAKE TWO IDENTICAL GIRDERS FOR EACH SPAN. PAINT MATT GREY.

GIRDERS ASSEMBLED
GUSSET PLATES
FLOOR GIRDER
FIT CARD GUSSET PLATES AS SHOWN. FLOOR GIRDERS ARE CUT FROM 1/8 INCH SQUARE STRIPWOOD (FOR OO GAUGE) AND GLUED INTO POSITION.

MAKE BALLAST BOARD TO FIT ON TOP OF FLOOR GIRDERS AND BETWEEN GUSSET PLATES. IT SHOULD BE AT LEAST 1/4 INCH LONGER THAN SPAN.
GUSSET PLATE
FLOOR GIRDER
WOODEN BALLAST BOARD
BALLAST
SLEEPER
BALLAST RETAINING STRIP
7 FT.
5 FT. 6 INS.
16 FT. 3 INS.
SECTION, WITH DIMENSIONS, OF FULL SIZE SINGLE TRACK SPAN (NOT TO SCALE)

ABUTMENTS MADE OF WOOD — SHOULD BE DESIGNED TO FIT THE SITE ON WHICH BRIDGE IS TO BE BUILT.
PEDESTALS REST ON THIS LEDGE
BEVEL
BEVEL
MAKE ABUTMENTS FROM FOUR PIECES OF WOOD. JOIN WITH GLUE. PAINT CONCRETE COLOUR.
THE EXTRA LENGTH ALLOWED ON BALLAST BOARD ENABLES SPAN TO OBTAIN STRONG SUPPORT AT ABUTMENTS.

TRACK
FASHION PEDESTALS FROM WOOD. FIT ON LEDGE AS SHOWN TO SUPPORT GIRDER ENDS.
ABUTMENT

Nº 10 AN AMERICAN CONTROL TOWER (SIGNAL CABIN)

THIS MODEL WILL MAKE AN ATTRACTIVE ADDITION TO ANY BRITISH TYPE LAY-OUT. THESE TOWERS ARE POSITIONED AT JUNCTIONS, CROSSINGS AND AT THE ENTRANCE TO YARDS ON PROTOTYPE AMERICAN RAILROADS. BUILD MODEL OF CARD AND STRIPWOOD, USING GENERAL METHODS OF CONSTRUCTION ALREADY DESCRIBED IN THIS SERIES. THE SCALE WILL ENABLE YOU TO MEASURE UP ALL DETAILS. GLAZE WINDOWS BY CEMENTING CELLOPHANE ON INSIDE, BEFORE FIXING WOODEN STRENGTHENING STRIPS FOR CORNERS IN PLACE.

DETAILS OF FOUR SIDES OF TOWER, WITH SCALE FROM WHICH TO WORK.
COVER ROOF WITH GREY TILE PAPER
DOTTED LINES SHOW EXTENT OF WALLS AND WINDOWS BENEATH EAVES.
CARD, OR WOOD STRIP
FORM PANEL FRAMES FROM THIN CARD AND CEMENT INTO PLACE
FRONT ELEVATION FACING TRACK
RIGHT END ELEVATION
REAR ELEVATION
LEFT END ELEVATION
USE THIS SCALE TO MEASURE OFF ALL THE DETAILS
0   5   10   15   20   25
SCALE IN FEET
USE POSTER OR SHOWCARD COLOURS FOR PAINTING. CHOOSE YOUR OWN COLOUR SCHEME. HERE ARE SOME SUGGESTIONS: WHITE OR CREAM WITH BROWN TRIM. APPLE GREEN WITH DARK GREEN. CHROME YELLOW WITH INDIAN RED. TWO SHADES OF GREY.

TOWER WALLS CUT FROM ONE PIECE OF CARD, DOORS AND WINDOWS CUT BEFORE WALLS ARE FOLDED.
STRIPWOOD STRENGTHENERS
SHELLAC INSIDE AND OUT. STRENGTHEN BY CEMENTING STRIPWOOD INSIDE EACH CORNER

BASE UPON WHICH TOWER IS CEMENTED. PLANKING FORMED WITH CARD STRIPS OR WOODEN SPILLS CUT TO CORRECT WIDTH, AND CEMENTED IN POSITION ON THREE SUPPORTING BEAMS. COLOUR: CREOSOTE.
PLANKING
STRIPWOOD BEAMS

METHOD FOR ASSEMBLING STEPS
CARD TREADS CEMENTED ON EACH STEP.
PLACE STRINGERS ON EITHER SIDE OF THIN WOOD STRIP CUT TO CORRECT WIDTH. DRIVE PINS ALONG OUTER EDGES OF STRINGERS TO HOLD THEM IN PLACE. CEMENT TREADS IN NOTCHES AND WHEN DRY, REMOVE WOOD STRIP.
CARD STRINGERS. WHEN CUTTING THESE, MAKE SURE THEY MATCH.

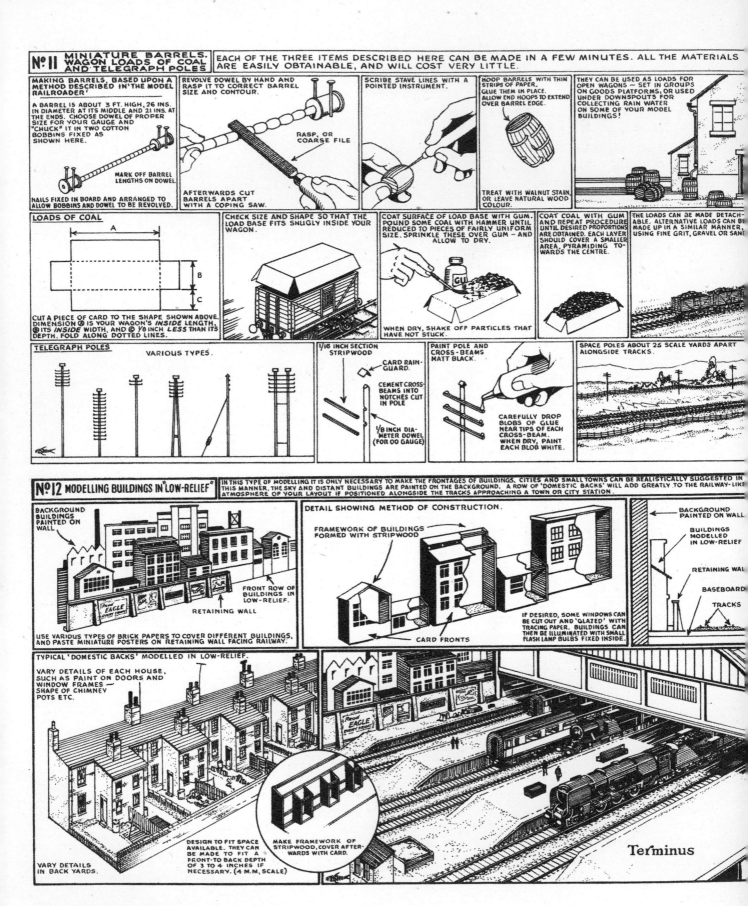

Nº II MINIATURE BARRELS. WAGON LOADS OF COAL AND TELEGRAPH POLES

EACH OF THE THREE ITEMS DESCRIBED HERE CAN BE MADE IN A FEW MINUTES. ALL THE MATERIALS ARE EASILY OBTAINABLE, AND WILL COST VERY LITTLE.

MAKING BARRELS, BASED UPON A METHOD DESCRIBED IN 'THE MODEL RAILROADER'

A BARREL IS ABOUT 3 FT. HIGH, 26 INS. IN DIAMETER AT ITS MIDDLE AND 21 INS. AT THE ENDS. CHOOSE DOWEL OF PROPER SIZE FOR YOUR GAUGE AND "CHUCK" IT IN TWO COTTON BOBBINS FIXED AS SHOWN HERE.

MARK OFF BARREL LENGTHS ON DOWEL

NAILS FIXED IN BOARD AND ARRANGED TO ALLOW BOBBINS AND DOWEL TO BE REVOLVED.

REVOLVE DOWEL BY HAND AND RASP IT TO CORRECT BARREL SIZE AND CONTOUR.

RASP, OR COARSE FILE

AFTERWARDS CUT BARRELS APART WITH A COPING SAW.

SCRIBE STAVE LINES WITH A POINTED INSTRUMENT.

HOOP BARRELS WITH THIN STRIPS OF PAPER. GLUE THEM IN PLACE. ALLOW END HOOPS TO EXTEND OVER BARREL EDGE.

TREAT WITH WALNUT STAIN, OR LEAVE NATURAL WOOD COLOUR.

THEY CAN BE USED AS LOADS FOR OPEN WAGONS — SET IN GROUPS ON GOODS PLATFORMS, OR USED UNDER DOWNSPOUTS FOR COLLECTING RAIN WATER ON SOME OF YOUR MODEL BUILDINGS!

LOADS OF COAL

CUT A PIECE OF CARD TO THE SHAPE SHOWN ABOVE. DIMENSION Ⓐ IS YOUR WAGON'S INSIDE LENGTH, Ⓑ ITS INSIDE WIDTH, AND Ⓒ 1/8 INCH LESS THAN ITS DEPTH. FOLD ALONG DOTTED LINES.

CHECK SIZE AND SHAPE SO THAT THE LOAD BASE FITS SNUGLY INSIDE YOUR WAGON.

COAT SURFACE OF LOAD BASE WITH GUM. POUND SOME COAL WITH HAMMER UNTIL REDUCED TO PIECES OF FAIRLY UNIFORM SIZE. SPRINKLE THESE OVER GUM — AND ALLOW TO DRY.

WHEN DRY, SHAKE OFF PARTICLES THAT HAVE NOT STUCK.

COAT COAL WITH GUM AND REPEAT PROCEDURE UNTIL DESIRED PROPORTIONS ARE OBTAINED. EACH LAYER SHOULD COVER A SMALLER AREA, PYRAMIDING TOWARDS THE CENTRE.

THE LOADS CAN BE MADE DETACHABLE. ALTERNATIVE LOADS CAN BE MADE UP IN A SIMILAR MANNER, USING FINE GRIT, GRAVEL OR SAND.

TELEGRAPH POLES

VARIOUS TYPES.

1/16 INCH SECTION STRIPWOOD

CARD RAIN-GUARD.

CEMENT CROSS-BEAMS INTO NOTCHES CUT IN POLE

1/8 INCH DIAMETER DOWEL (FOR OO GAUGE)

PAINT POLE AND CROSS-BEAMS MATT BLACK.

CAREFULLY DROP BLOBS OF GLUE NEAR TIPS OF EACH CROSS-BEAM. WHEN DRY, PAINT EACH BLOB WHITE.

SPACE POLES ABOUT 25 SCALE YARDS APART ALONGSIDE TRACKS.

Nº I2 MODELLING BUILDINGS IN "LOW-RELIEF"

IN THIS TYPE OF MODELLING IT IS ONLY NECESSARY TO MAKE THE FRONTAGES OF BUILDINGS. CITIES AND SMALL TOWNS CAN BE REALISTICALLY SUGGESTED IN THIS MANNER. THE SKY AND DISTANT BUILDINGS ARE PAINTED ON THE BACKGROUND. A ROW OF 'DOMESTIC BACKS' WILL ADD GREATLY TO THE RAILWAY-LIKE ATMOSPHERE OF YOUR LAYOUT IF POSITIONED ALONGSIDE THE TRACKS APPROACHING A TOWN OR CITY STATION.

BACKGROUND BUILDINGS PAINTED ON WALL

FRONT ROW OF BUILDINGS IN LOW-RELIEF.

RETAINING WALL

USE VARIOUS TYPES OF BRICK PAPERS TO COVER DIFFERENT BUILDINGS, AND PASTE MINIATURE POSTERS ON RETAINING WALL FACING RAILWAY.

DETAIL SHOWING METHOD OF CONSTRUCTION.

FRAMEWORK OF BUILDINGS FORMED WITH STRIPWOOD

CARD FRONTS

IF DESIRED, SOME WINDOWS CAN BE CUT OUT AND 'GLAZED' WITH TRACING PAPER. BUILDINGS CAN THEN BE ILLUMINATED WITH SMALL FLASH LAMP BULBS FIXED INSIDE.

BACKGROUND PAINTED ON WALL

BUILDINGS MODELLED IN LOW-RELIEF

RETAINING WALL

BASEBOARD

TRACKS

TYPICAL 'DOMESTIC BACKS' MODELLED IN LOW-RELIEF.

VARY DETAILS OF EACH HOUSE, SUCH AS PAINT ON DOORS AND WINDOW FRAMES — SHAPE OF CHIMNEY POTS ETC.

VARY DETAILS IN BACK YARDS.

DESIGN TO FIT SPACE AVAILABLE. THEY CAN BE MADE TO FIT A FRONT-TO-BACK DEPTH OF 3 TO 4 INCHES IF NECESSARY. (4 M.M. SCALE)

MAKE FRAMEWORK OF STRIPWOOD, COVER AFTERWARDS WITH CARD.

Terminus

Sherlock Holmes — new style

How Science solves the problems of present-day detection.

By George Howard. Illustrated by Dudley Pout.

MOST of us have been thrilled with the exploits of Sherlock Holmes as the most famous detective of all solves mysteries which have baffled the police – not to mention his friend Dr Watson. With the help of his magnifying glass, his retorts, and his learned books on poisons and so on, the sleuth unravels the mystery.

If we ever see a real-life detective it is unlikely that he will be carrying a magnifying glass or any other piece of scientific apparatus. In fact, we may be inclined to think that Holmes was rather far-fetched. Actually, the modern scientific detective is more fortunate than Conan Doyle's famous character. He waits in his laboratory for the police to bring the clues to him. There he has instruments which would turn the sleuth of Baker Street green with envy.

This is a very great change indeed. Long after the Sherlock Holmes stories were written a police commissioner taking over his appointment at Scotland Yard found that the only piece of scientific apparatus in the whole place was a rather battered old microscope worth 3s. 6d! But since the youngest of us was born a great new network of scientific laboratories has been built up to see that the wrong-doer will be found out.

One of these laboratories is in Scotland Yard itself, but those of us who live in provincial towns may be rather surprised to know that there are others at Birmingham, Bristol, Cardiff, Nottingham, Preston and Wakefield. They are not very imposing buildings. They do their work quietly, and it's more than likely that we have never seen them.

In addition to these laboratories which work on behalf of our police and are organized by the Home Office, the Government Department which looks after our well-being and sees that law and order are maintained, there are many others, some run by other Government Departments and still more by private firms in the chemical and engineering industries, at our universities and so on. Just as it is the duty of every one of us to help the police with information, these scientists put their skill at the disposal of the police when required.

It is unlikely that visitors will be allowed to any of

them, so the next best thing is to come on a word-picture tour. Probably the most interesting of all these laboratories detecting evil-doing is the Department of the Government Chemist, which is in a rather murky building very close to the Law Courts in London, and will interest historians as well as budding scientists – for it is the oldest laboratory of its kind in the world.

It all began more than a hundred years ago when the subjects of young Queen Victoria complained that all sorts of strange leaves were going into their tobacco. To find out what was going on the Government told some chemists to examine samples of tobacco. The manufacturers laughed until, with a few simple instruments, these scientific detectives correctly identified oak leaves, rhubarb leaves, sand, treacle, and many other substances added for weight.

The same laboratory is always at work to see that your food and clothes are good. Half a million samples are examined every year. They range from pats of butter taken from a restaurant to sports shirts, from poultry meal to petrol.

Let's watch the "back room men" at work on some ordinary foodstuffs. Here is a piece of butter being tested to see if any margarine has been unlawfully added. A tiny smear is chemically tested for the presence of nickel. That metal is always present in margarine – it is used to harden it – and analysis will detect even such a tiny quantity as one part of nickel in 250,000 parts of margarine. Butter, of course, has no nickel in it.

Next to him is another white-coated young scientist at work on a pot of jam. He has a specially designed lamp the rays of which cause the ingredients of the jam to fluoresce – that is to say, they make them shine with a particular glow according to the fruit used. Apple pulp is the usual material used to increase the bulk of jam, and it must not, of course, be added if the label on the jar says that only strawberries have been used. Now apples contain a substance called malic acid. It fluoresces with a bright blue light. If such a hue is found then there must be some apples in the jam.

The same rays are used to find out if wheat flour has been spoiled with soya beans or rye, and to see if there is any chicory in 'pure' coffee. No matter how tiny is the proportion of the illegal substance that tell-tale glow will indicate its presence.

Sometimes this laboratory is asked to settle disputes about food. There was once a man who walked into a Scottish baker's shop with a half-used loaf he had bought there. "Look at this," he complained; "there is

a rat hair in the bread. The place where you keep the flour must be overrun with vermin."

Tha was a very serious reflection on the bakery and the proprietor could not believe it. He suspected that the man was trying to get compensation by a trick and he asked that the hair be examined and identified.

Under the microscope, when the hair had been cut, the expert was able to say that the hair came from a rabbit. Not even this dishonest customer was prepared to suggest that the bakery was overrun with rabbits!

Now let's make a tour of the laboratories working solely on behalf of police investigations. One where we can fairly easily understand what is going on is busily detecting poisons. It is not unlike a school laboratory: the same sort of tables, equipped with bunsen burners, running water, retorts, clamps, and test tubes. The way poisons are detected is very similar to the simple experiments of every chemistry class finding out whether some substance like iron or salt is present.

One thing we learn right away disillusions us about some of the tales concerning mysterious poisons used by native tribes in faraway places, or by the mad scientist wreaking his vengeance on his victims. They are just ideas of the writers of such tales. There is no such thing as an unknown poison: every one of them falls into a particular class, details of which are well known.

Most of the work on poisons concerns accidents. Perhaps some food has gone bad, a child has eaten some berries during a country walk, or chemicals have tainted foodstuffs stacked nearby. All that the chemists need is a piece of the suspected food, a smear from a spoon or plate, or a few drops of liquid from a cup or glass.

Like his colleague working on food substitutes, the poison detective makes much use of a fluorescent lamp. He simply shines an ultra-violet ray lamp on the specimen and checks the colour. Let's see an example of this work, with a non-poisonous substance. The chemist takes two bottles of milk and draws off a drop from each, placing them on a slide. The room is darkened and the lamp switched on. The light is dim, but the two drops of liquid begin to glow. One, which is pure milk, shines like snow on a sunlit field; the other has a ring of violet light at the edges. That is because an aspirin tablet was placed in the second bottle. Ultra-violet rays will detect aspirin even though there is only one part to several millions of milk. In fact, if you dropped one tablet in a big churn at the dairy, it could be detected in the thousands of milk jugs of the customers a few hours later.

Once a little girl became very ill after playing in the fields in springtime. She was too young to explain what

Chief Superintendent Cherrill of the Fingerprint Branch, Scotland Yard, examining fingerprints on an automatic pistol.

she had eaten, though the doctor was quite certain that this was the trouble. Hurriedly a laboratory was asked to check some transparent fluid separated from her blood. It glowed with a yellow light. A search of the fields where she had been showed many celandines in bloom. One of these flowers was placed beside the child's blood fluid and it glowed with exactly the same yellow light. It was this plant which had made the little girl ill.

In order to ascertain how much poison is present retorts and test tubes are used. Various chemicals will cause the poison to precipitate, colour a liquid, or give off fumes as the case may be. Such an investigation may mean twenty or more tests before the results mentioned in the standard reports are obtained and the poison identified.

Forgery is a crime which needs the help of the scientific detective – and it is a subject where anyone can try his hand in being a modern Sherlock Holmes once he has some knowledge. You can have a lot of fun challenging your friends to write extra words in some old exercise book, add some more brush strokes to an old painting, or say you will identify different pens used on the same piece of writing.

People who copy other people's writing have three

methods of doing so. One way is to put the writing to be copied on top of a piece of glass with a powerful light underneath. Then with a clean piece of paper he copies the words he wants.

That is easily detected if you have a magnifying glass of reasonable power. Anyone writing the words *Eagle Annual* in his own hand will lift the pen only once: between the two words. But in copying there will be several occasions when he stops writing to make sure that he is tracing the letters correctly. These breaks will easily be seen under the glass.

Another way is to trace the writing on to a blank piece of paper underneath the original, pressing hard so that there are dents to copy. Then the writing is filled in. Under a magnifying glass these dents will be seen as well as the writing, for no one copies exactly. The third method is to practice over and over again until it is possible to imitate the original well. This is more difficult to detect, and needs a powerful microscope. Then the width of the strokes of the original are compared with that of the suspected copy. Unless the same pen has been used and the same angle adopted to hold it there will be a marked contrast.

If you have access to two typewriters, even of the same make, you will be amazed how different the letters appear under a glass. Perhaps a hair has got stuck to the letter *E* and caused a tiny break in the edging. It won't be present on an *E* typed on the second machine. Letters get slightly out of straight, their ends get battered – and always in some manner not found on another machine.

I NKS and papers need the resources of a police laboratory for satisfactory identification. Inks gradually change colour through the action of the air and it is possible to grade the shade to estimate how long it has been there. Another wonderful machine will even measure how far it has soaked into the paper, which continues gradually for many months. For old documents which someone may pretend he had found in an attic there is one date of which he must be very careful. In 1868 a type of ink containing nigrosine was invented and became universal. Its presence can be detected by chemical reaction instantly. Anyone trying to forge a document supposedly written before 1868 is set with a problem. He must not use a nigrosine ink, and it is impossible for him to purchase a black ink without it!

Even if he makes his own ink the scientific detective still has many tricks up his sleeve to expose him. Not so long ago someone produced some documents on which in faded brown ink was the signature of William Penn, founder of Pennsylvania in the United States. He had made a splendid ink, and he had managed to fade it beautifully. But under the microscope minute specks of steel were seen. A tiny piece of the signature taken out and treated chemically revealed the presence of silver. The steel specks came from a steel nib; the silver from the ink and used to give a brown effect. In William Penn's day there were no steel nibs and they certainly did not waste silver in the ink!

No doubt you have often been exasperated when trying to make a neat erasure of ink or pencil in your schoolwork. The laboratory men will tell you that, from their point of view, a really perfect erasure is quite impossible. Try rubbing a pencil mark out of a piece of good quality notepaper and then look at it under a good magnifying glass. You will see that the fibres of the paper have been pushed in every direction, in contrast to the neat lines of the unused paper. There will also be specks of pencil carbon buried in the cracks and crannies quite invisible to the naked eye.

Ink stains removed with a chemical remover are still visible once the laboratory gets hold of the paper. Once again the ultra-violet lamp is brought into use. A glow from the chemical bleacher will immediately be seen, and usually a faint ghost-like image of the deleted writing will also show. This writing can, in any case, be developed with iodine vapour.

The paper itself tells a long and fascinating story. The linen, rags, wood pulp, or esparto grass used in its manufacture can easily be indentified, and no paper from two paper mills will be the same. Even the same paper from the same mill, but produced at a different period, will have marked differences when subject to very high magnification.

Water marks are impossible to copy properly. The letters or picture to be seen on every piece of plain paper are made during manufacture while the pulp is still wet. The only way to imitate it later is to press it on a wax copy of the water-mark. This wax will stop coloured water soaking into it in quite a different manner from the real watermark. By taking a piece of genuine paper and a piece of suspected paper and watching the soaking under fluorescent light the different movement is easily noted.

No doubt you have often seen writing appear in reverse colours on paper burning in the grate. As soon as you touch it the paper crumbles. But at Scotland Yard two experts have devised a method of reading everything on charred paper. The scraps are placed between two sheets of glass treated with chemicals. They are then slowly cooked until the paper is reduced to ash. The writing remains on the glass in yellow markings. An easier method used when the paper is not in too many pieces is to treat it with chloral hydrate and glycerine. Dried very carefully in a draughtless cupboard the writing appears in black and the charred pieces return to their orignal white.

I N the case of forgery of paintings you can obtain a good clue to the scientific method by examining your own attempt at adding some brush strokes to an older picture. Even if you get the shade right, close examination will show that the later brush marks are on top of the older ones, and if you have a very accurate micrometer it may even be possible to measure the difference in thickness.

The forgery of old masters is fairly common, and the police are asked to check whether the suspicion is correct. X-rays are used as a preliminary check. As it is usually necessary to paint the faked picture on an old canvas the forger will obtain some painting from the period of the artist he intends to imitate. This earlier picture will show up as a shadowed outline under X-rays. Sometimes the crooked artist is very careless. In the case of a forgery of a Franz Hals picture (he was the artist who painted the famous Laughing Cavalier)

X-rays showed modern nails under the oils, which the forger had used to hold down his rather tattered and ancient canvas to the frame. The metal naturally showed up clearly.

Another method used is to insert a hollow needle into the picture. The hole it makes is almost invisible, but the section of paint and canvas thus obtained is ample

less – most obligingly so that we can see most of the laboratory processes in action!

He has left an old coat behind through being alarmed. There are fingerprints on a drawer he opened with some kind of tool, and in his tussle with the lock he cut his hand, leaving a blob of blood nearby. Like most burglars he was not above refreshment during his nefarious

Comparing shoes with a plaster cast of footprints taken at the scene of crime.

for analysis. The chemists have tables of the chemical constituents of oils and water colours, as well as the fibres of canvas, for every period of art taken from known genuine pictures, and in this way the exact age of the materials under examination can be convincingly checked.

Even the wooden frame can be made to tell its story. Old timber shines with a white glow under fluorescent light. New wood has hardly any glow at all.

Now let us watch the scientists at work on one of their urgent tasks. The police have brought such clues as they have been able to find at the scene of the crime. They want to know everything possible about them. To us there may not seem very much to tell. We are told that it is a case of burglary. The robber has been very care-

activities, and there is a cigarette end and a half empty glass in the room.

Such a wealth of – to us – ordinary clues are the laboratory's dream. Every one of them will provide a graphic story. Let us watch the coat being examined. Detectives have already taken down details of its make, size and possible age, and are going the rounds of the shops. The laboratory intends to find out its story since it was bought.

First of all it is put in a paper bag and beaten to remove the dust. This dust, together with more obtained by running over it with a tiny vacuum cleaner, is analysed. The grains of dust will be identified and provide clues to the man's occupation and place of residence. There may be brick dust, showing that he has worked on building construction, and it will show from what bricks it comes. There may be grains of tobacco in the pockets and the brand will be ascertainable. Grass seeds which become embedded in the cloth may show a particular locality where that grass is common. There will be a dozen other clues in this dust.

Next the stains on the coat are analysed. They may be petrol, benzol, drinks, food, or paint – all almost invisible to the naked eye, but clearly seen and identified under special lamps. A piece will be taken out and subjected to chemical reaction to find out if the coat has been dry cleaned, and if so by what process and how long ago.

Measurements of the creases will enable a good description of the man's build to be given, and a picture of his general bodily appearance drawn.

The fingerprints are of value mainly if the burglar has been in the hands of the police previously. If you examine your thumb – where the marks are clearer than on the fingers – you will see the contours which are called papilliary ridges. They contain tiny holes which continuously exude perspiration even if your thumb is cold. It takes some training to note the major differences, but if you examine your thumb beside that of a friend's you will probably get a general idea. There are seven main types of contour: a short one, a dot, a lake, a ridge terminating upwards, another terminating downwards, and a split upwards or downwards. Then there is a general appearance of loops and arches which vary. No one, so far as is known, ever has the same pattern as anyone else.

To make the prints clear for photographing two kinds of powder are used. For polished surfaces a grey one is needed. It consists of metallic mercury and powdered chalk. On light surfaces such as white paint the detectives use powdered graphite. You can make this by scraping a hard pencil very finely.

In the laboratory it is possible to find prints on cloth and paper. The material is dusted with charcoal powder and photographed with a powerful light played on the spot at an angle. On soft surfaces, such as a piece of soap, cheese, or similar foodstuff ultra-violet light will throw the print into relief for the camera.

The tool used to prise open the drawer has probably been used for something else. Infra-red rays will show up any maker's name which has been filed off. A wonderful machine called a spectroscope will measure the part of the spectrum occupied by the colour of any stain, specks of paint, oil, and so on, and identify it.

The blood, the cigarette end, and the glass will tell a story of the burglar he can never disguise. The saliva on the cigarette end and on the edge of the glass, like the spot of blood, will give the blood group. If, for example, the glass indicates "A" group, and the blood stain "O", while the cigarette end is "B", then three people must have been in that room. Incidentally it is impossible to wash away blood sufficiently well to foil the scientific detective. The washed out stain on a handkerchief or a piece of cloth will show up clearly under infra-red rays, and by chemical treatment the blood group can be identified.

If our burglar had touched the window top with his head and left a single strand of hair there we could learn still more. Our friends could tell whether it had been pulled out or fallen out. It would show at one end how it had been cut, and the racial origin of its owner would be known. Any dressing on it could be analysed.

Within a few hours a vivid picture of the wanted man would be in the hands of the police. Though these scientific clues are not usually the evidence given in court to ensure punishment of the wrong-doer they are the material by which the police get an idea of whom they must try to find. It is little wonder that the miscreant, when he is finally arrested, is dumbfounded with the facts that the police already know. He learns that doing wrong is almost certainly bound to bring quick and certain retribution – but he does not know of the quiet, clever work which has gone on among a team of scientists he will never meet to bring about his arrest.

KEEPER: "Clear off, my lad, fishing's not allowed here."
JACK: "I'm not fishing, sir, I'm only drowning worms!"

LANDLADY: "Look here, young man, you must either pay your bill, or leave."
GUEST: "Oh, thank you, Mrs Peck, my last landlady made me do both!"

Rocket Pioneer

The story of
MAX VALIER

BY J. E. PRYDE-HUGHES · ILLUSTRATIONS BY WALTER PANNET

NO sooner had man achieved flight than imaginative fellows turned their thoughts to other ways of mastering passage through the air at ever increasing speeds, at greater heights, and in immensely bigger machines. The experiences of the First World War gave a push to the new, and at first fanciful, ideas of air travel at great speeds, and brought forward the fantasy of trips to the Moon and other planets. About this time various scientifically minded men were playing with the notion of rocket propulsion. Some wrote seriously about the theory and its applications to passenger-carrying aircraft; but it was a young aviator, whose enthusiasm for rockets was greeted with sarcasm, who first put his theories to the test and proved their possibilities.

Max Valier was a young Austrian aviator who had had many flying adventures. Once he came down in a flaming plane from which he was dragged scorched and with broken ribs and other injuries. That day his life was all but ended. Had it been so, the value of his later experiments with rockets would have been lost: for Valier, though scoffed at, actually built a machine that was driven by rockets in several tests and proved that rockets could be harnessed to drive a heavier-than-air body. In a later and more ambitious attempt at speed, he was unfortunately killed.

Until his death few had taken much notice of Valier's trials, and when he died his work was forgotten except

by one or two unseen observers, who obviously later applied the knowledge obtained to purposes other than those imagined by the zealous young pioneer. And it is perhaps natural that at times he was a bit impatient of the hesitations of established scientists and engineers who were inclined to belittle his theories and designs.

When after the First World War, Valier was free to work on his theories he was far from rich. To support himself and carry on his experiments, he had to put his hand and mind to all sorts of ways and means, for he could find no one to back his ideas. Whichever way he looked he met with indifference and not a little scorn. Nevertheless, lonely and practically single-handed he carried on as far as his poor resources would allow. He wrote articles, delivered lectures, sketched, and in fact dealt with anything and everything likely to bring in some money, or attract attention to his work.

Even when in 1928 attempts to reach high speed with rockets practically failed, and a newspaper voiced the general opinion in an article headed: "And now, farewell to rocket propulsion", he would not give up for, as he pointed out, it took a century for the railway locomotive to develop as the efficient machine that it is today, and motor cars and aeroplanes had seen many years of research and experience.

Isaac Walton had the idea of constructing a special steam boiler with exhaust tubes and nozzle to propel a rocket type of steam car, and Charles Golightly, over a hundred years ago, suggested a kind of rocket flying-machine driven by a steam jet forced out of a cylindrical boiler. Such ideas were played with for a long time, but now the true rocket motor propelled by a fluid fuel exploded in a chamber and the gases generated being forced out through a nozzle makes those earlier ideas seem absurd.

A space-ship, as we all know, has not to depend on external air-resistance, as does the usual aircraft, but given sufficiently high starting speeds would be able to

He also proposed a speed contest with the famous motor-boat racer Segrave. Scarcely knowing which way to turn for aid, Valier clung desperately to his project and experiments. With a couple of friends he founded a company in Breslau called the "Union of Space Ship Travel", with the object of having a working centre for making appeals and creating interest. Then, soon after, he arranged with an expert record-holding pilot to join him in his first flight and to help him in the equipment of a machine with auxiliary rocket-tubes.

The Dynamit A/G, of Munich, placed explosives at his disposal for experimental purposes, and moreover, gave him freedom to experiment at their factories. Experts in ballistics now tended to agree with Valier's opinions of the possibility of rockets, that, in fact, as far as energy and ballistics were concerned the theory

The dramatic and successful conclusion to Max Valier's early experiments. Across the frozen lake of Starnberg his rocket projected sled dashes at great speed and satisfies him and his critics as to the practical possibilities of rocket-propulsion.

rise beyond the earth's atmosphere and sail in space. Valier had hopes of building such a craft and of making the initial flight himself; but he protested when suggestions were put out that he proposed to make an attempt to "shoot" himself on to the moon. His first big trip, if his initial flights were successful, was to be a jump from Berlin to New York in two hours, and in this aim he was quite earnest. In fact, while still struggling to find the money to build the first rocket-machine, he issued speed challenges, and offered to make the first test projection across the English Channel, if anyone would back the construction of a rocket-plane according to his designs.

was sound. It was while experimenting with solid fuels that Valier became convinced that a ship to fly in space could only be envisaged when the problem of the use of liquid fuel was solved. Nevertheless, he continued feverishly with the materials at hand and at the same time set to work planning giant space ships.

He also designed a single-seater airplane for making his first attempt on a flight, or leap, across the English Channel from France. It was at this time that he issued his speed test challenge to Segrave, the world famous motor-boat racer, so confident was he, but the challenge was ignored. In any case Valier had first to obtain money with which to build his rocket-craft, and then complete and test the machine. It was not enough to have ideas, designs and details down on paper, for however attractive they might look they proved nothing, and only factual flight would satisfy the unconverted.

Without sufficient money to construct his aircraft Valier used that which he had in building a sled, mounting an engine which consisted in the main of a battery

before him he pressed on the starting lever. The first rocket exploded with a terrific roar as the sled shot forward like a shell from a gun, leaving behind a trail of smoke and flame which hid the machine for a second or so. Then it was seen that the sled was under control and was sleeking over the ice with speed and ease; the succeeding rockets exploded rhythmically in turn, and unofficial timekeepers gave out that the speed of the sled at one time approached 300 m.p.h., a remarkable feat in

A drawing based on Max Valier's own sketches for his rocket propelled single-seater aircraft and in which he hoped to fly the English Channel.

of rocket tubes in a drum which looked like the cartridge chamber of a giant revolver. By means of automatic control the drum turned as each rocket exploded so that a new rocket came into place for the subsequent explosion in the series.

His first practical test was on the frozen lake of Starnberg, in Bavaria. There were few to cheer the intrepid inventor, but those who did witness what was to them a reckless adventure, were repaid for their interest. With the calm of his conviction, Valier brought out onto the ice the frail sled with its rather cumbersome Rocket machinery in the tail, and without any ado he made sure all was in order and seated himself for the trial. Quietly he gave the order to stand clear. Much depended on his trial, and it was not any fear of accident that made him serious and grave. With the course now open

those days, for remember this was some years before Hitler revealed his war-like purpose, and 250 m.p.h. was still considered a good speed for airplanes. Whatever speed the rocket-driven sled actually attained it certainly seemed to skim across the smooth surface of the ice-bound lake like a fiery demon spitting flame and smoke from the rockets as each went off.

Valier was satisfied. He had proved that rocket drive was within reach; the apparatus was still intact, and he himself unharmed and unperturbed. He was, too, somewhat relieved and elated by his success.

For success it proved to be, his first real success after years of weary preaching and working, trial and failure, hope and disappointment, borne up only by his belief in his theories. Engineers began to show some interest, and undoubtedly, as after events suggest, there were scientists and technicians slyly observing and checking all that took place. Soon it became clear that the great motorcar manufacturers, Opels, were impressed. They offered Valier facilities for further experiments, now with an automobile-type chassis on wheels. In time a suitable light-framed carriage was built into which Valier fitted his revolver-like explosion chambers to be operated by compressed gases, yet still on the rocket principle. This car was fitted to travel on rails and a number of runs were made, but no great speeds were reached.

Opels, of course, had in view the possibility of utilising Valier's principles, if not his systems, in the powering of ordinary automobiles on the road. A similar car to the first was fitted up and tests made when a real effort was determined on to find out what speeds could be reached.

What went wrong no one can say. The car was brought out. The apparatus was checked and found in order. Valier took his seat. The car started with a great leap forward then to the horror of the witnesses, who all had hoped for spectacular results of the trial, but not such as now happened, the car was rent and blown to pieces by an explosion. Investigation and reconstruction failed to reveal what had caused the disaster. It can only be supposed that one of the exhaust tubes jammed, and the rocket, fired inside the car, set off all the other rockets.

So, a brave young man died. Had he lived he would have become for sure, a leading figure in the world of jet and rocket propulsion. What he achieved gave his unquenchable spirit some cheer and comfort, and repaid him in a way, for all his struggles, the adversity he had to meet. Though after his death his ideas seemed to lose interest, there is little doubt that those scientists who eventually, during the second World War, developed the V1 and V2 rockets which threatened disaster to fighters for freedom, drew much on Valier's work and experiences.

TRY IT YOURSELF . . .   BY SATCHELL

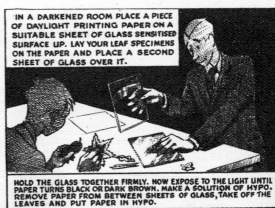

IN A DARKENED ROOM PLACE A PIECE OF DAYLIGHT PRINTING PAPER ON A SUITABLE SHEET OF GLASS SENSITISED SURFACE UP. LAY YOUR LEAF SPECIMENS ON THE PAPER AND PLACE A SECOND SHEET OF GLASS OVER IT.

HOLD THE GLASS TOGETHER FIRMLY. NOW EXPOSE TO THE LIGHT UNTIL PAPER TURNS BLACK OR DARK BROWN. MAKE A SOLUTION OF HYPO. REMOVE PAPER FROM BETWEEN SHEETS OF GLASS, TAKE OFF THE LEAVES AND PUT PAPER IN HYPO.

THIS WILL FIX YOUR PRINTS. YOU WILL HAVE A DETAILED PRINT OF YOUR LEAVES SHOWING ALL THE VEINS AND PORES IN WHITE ON A BLACK BACKGROUND

PASTE THE PRINTS IN A BOOK AND WRITE THE NAMES OF THE TREES TO WHICH THE LEAVES BELONG UNDER EACH PRINT

THE FLYING CRUSADERS

A new BIGGLES story by W. E. Johns

ILLUSTRATED BY HAROLD W. HAILSTONE

OUTSIDE the Air Police Operations Headquarters a summer sun glinted on the polished surfaces of sundry aircraft parked on the concrete apron. Through them, cap in hand, walked Air Constable Algy Lacey after a routine test flight. "Seems a pity to spend a day like this fiddling with filing cabinets," he observed, striding into the office where Air Constables "Ginger" Hebblethwaite and "Bertie" Lissie were working on index cards.

"You can all go down to the country for the weekend if you like," offered Biggles from his desk, where he was dealing with the morning mail. "I may take a run out myself."

"And do what ?" inquired Ginger.

Biggles smiled. "We could have a busman's holiday by looking at some of the bamboo and piano-wire contraptions in which people staggered into the atmosphere before instruments were invented."

"Where's this ?" inquired Ginger. "I've always wanted to fly a birdcage."

"Mancroft Castle. Sir Giles Mancroft was one of the very early pioneers. When he got too old for the game he spent his money – too much, it seems, since he's having to sell up – making a collection of the early types of aircraft. He kept them in flying trim, too. I have an invitation to the auction on Saturday. Seems a pity to have to break up what must be a unique aviation museum. Incidentally, I see the sale includes the Flying Crusader, the machine in which, with a bit of luck, Sir Giles might have been first across the Channel. I seem to remember there was some trouble about that machine a few years ago, but I forget the details. I must look them up. I have a note here, too, from a fellow named Smithers, who used to be one of my mechanics in the war. He says he now works with Sir Giles and wants to see me. Presumably his visit has something to do with the sale. I hope he doesn't expect me to buy these old crates."

Biggles' fears were not realised, for some time later, when Smithers arrived, it was soon clear that his journey had been prompted by motives altogether different. "Seeing that you're coming to the auction, sir, and hearing you were in the Air Police, I took a chance that you might be able to help me," he explained.

"How did you know I was going to the auction?"

"I posted the invitations and saw your name on one," admitted Smithers frankly.

"And in what way can I help you?"

"By clearing my father's name. With the old Crusader being sold it'll be the last chance."

"Suppose you sit down and tell us about it?" suggested Biggles.

"WELL, sir, you must understand that there are two Flying Crusaders – or there were," began the ex-airman. "One is a 'plane and the other is a picture. No doubt one was called after the other. But I'd better warn you right away that the business that I'm going to to tell you about, in which they were both involved, takes a bit of believing now. You'll wonder, as I do sometimes, why this and that wasn't done at the time; but the war started bang in the middle of the affair and the police had something else to do; for which reason, I suppose, the case was soon dropped and was hardly mentioned in the papers. The first Flying Crusader was a picture presented to one of Sir Giles' ancestors by the Tsar of Russia at the time of the Crusades. It shows a knight in armour on a winged horse. It was quite small, but as it was painted by the most famous artist of the time I reckon it would be worth something to-day; enough to save Sir Giles having to sell the estate, if he could get it back."

"Where is the picture now?" inquired Biggles.

"That's what we'd like to know," answered Smithers sadly. "It disappeared in circumstances that really cost my father his life."

"How did that come about?"

"It was like this, sir. It happened at a house-party just two days before the war. Sir Giles gave the party to people interested in aviation to show off the old machines. One of the guests was an American named Silberman, who claimed to have been in the famous Escadrille Lafayette, the American squadron that fought for France in the early days of the first war. According to him at the inquiry this is what happened."

"Your father was employed by Sir Giles I take it?"

"Yes, sir, first as a mechanic and afterwards as his butler."

"I see. Go on."

"Silberman said that after he had gone to bed he found he had left his cigarette case in the library and went down to get it. The first thing he saw was that the Flying Crusader picture had been cut out of its frame. The window overlooking the park was open. From it he saw a light moving near the canvas hangars in which the old aircraft were housed. Thinking it might be the thief he ran down and caught the man, who turned out to be my father. According to Silberman my father attacked him. There was a fight, and that part was true, because not only did it end in my father being so terribly knocked about that he never recovered, but Silberman himself was in hospital for some time. A gamekeeper heard the noise and rushed in to find my father on the ground, and Silberman leaning against the old Crusader; which is why I think the 'plane had something to do with it. They were both carried off to hospital."

"Do I understand your father died without saying what happened?"

"Yes, sir. He had a head injury and never fully recovered consciousness up to the time he died a week or two later. All he could do was mutter something about the Flying Crusader. Of course, he wouldn't think of taking the picture. What made things look bad for him was, he was one of the few people who knew about the treasure supposed to be linked up with the painting. There was an old legend in the family that the picture was actually the key to a treasure which the first Sir Giles was supposed to have brought back from Russia. My father often suggested to the present Sir Giles that they took the picture out of the frame to have a closer look; but he wouldn't do anything about it. He'd just laugh and say the story was a lot of romantic nonsense."

"I see," said Biggles slowly. "What was your father supposed to be doing in the hangar when Silberman caught him there?"

"It was suggested that he was about to make off with the picture. To me that didn't make sense, but the way it was put at the inquiry it didn't sound so unreasonable because there were cars in the hangar. There wasn't room for all the guests' cars in the garage so some were put in the hangars."

"And what about the picture?"

"It was never found. There was a search made for it, but it was only half-hearted. The war was on and the police had something else to do. Sir Giles himself went off to war. Being on reserve I had to go. Silberman went back to America and the whole thing sort of fizzled out. Nobody really bothered. By the time my father died people were thinking more about being bombed."

"And what's your view of it?"

"I SAY it was Silberman who took the picture, not my father," declared Smithers. "It was the other way round. My father caught *him*. That's why I've come to you now, sir. Silberman killed my father to get that picture, and it struck me that if he hears about the sale he'll turn up on Saturday. That's if, as I believe, the old 'plane has something to do with the mystery."

"How do you know he hasn't already got the picture?"

"I don't see how he could have got it. If he had, we'd have heard about it by now. Something tells me that picture is linked up with the 'plane, and it's a long time since anyone saw the old Crusader. You see, by the time Silberman was out of hospital the war was in full swing. The castle was requisitioned by the government, so the old machines were dismantled and stored in the cellars with the furniture. Silberman couldn't have got to them there. The auction on Saturday will be the first time the 'planes have been seen in public.

"You're not suggesting that Silberman was going to *fly* away with the picture?"

"No. Why should he? His car was one of those parked in the hangar. I say Silberman was making for his car when my father caught up with him. He never got to the car. The picture wasn't in it, because the cars were searched the next day. Silberman, being in hospital, couldn't have got to it to move anything."

Biggles considered the matter. "All right Smithers," he said. "I see what you're driving at. We'll come down on Saturday and have a look round. By the way, have any of these machines been in the air recently?"

Smithers smiled. "Only the Flying Crusader. Yesterday, believe it or not, Sir Giles decided for old time's sake to have a last flip – only inside the grounds, of course. We put some fuel and oil in her. I didn't think she'd start; but lo and behold, off she went like a bird, and Sir Giles did a circuit at about ten feet."

"Good show," acknowledged Biggles, smiling. "Now

"Are you looking for something?" asked Biggles.

I shall certainly make a point of coming down on Saturday to have a look at her."

When Smithers had gone Biggles turned to the others. "If only for a day out I shall have to go down and put in a bid for this gallant old kite."

"Do you really want it?" inquired Ginger.

Biggles shook his head. "No. We've no room for antiques. But if somebody else wants her he'll have to bid against me; and the higher the bidding goes the more interested shall I become."

"You mean, if the picture thief is there you'll force him to show his hand?" suggested Algy.

"Either that or I'm going to land myself with an expensive souvenir in the shape of an extremely obsolete aircraft. Actually, you'd better do the bidding, Ginger. Someone in the crowd may recognise me and ask awkward questions if I'm seen doing it. Keep and eye on me, and keep bidding till I signal you to stop. I shall want to see who's bidding against you if the price gets high. You others can keep your eyes skinned, too."

"D'you seriously expect Silberman to be there, old boy?" inquired Bertie shrewdly, polishing his eyeglass.

"I don't know about that," replied Biggles pensively. "He might be. If he comes he'll probably be in some sort of disguise. After what happened at Mancroft Castle he'd hardly have the brass face to be seen in public, bidding for a machine near which, after all, he did kill a man. That would look mighty suspicious to some people. Newspapers have long memories, and reporters would soon be asking questions which Silberman might find embarrassing. He won't overlook that, you may be sure. We'll go down in the car."

MANCROFT Castle turned out to be a magnificent country seat set in parkland not far from the flat expanse of the Fens; but to Biggles and his assistants the point of interest was not the scenery but the row of veteran 'planes parked on a simple airstrip that fronted two delapidated canvas hangars. Gathered round them were interested spectators, a sprinkling of pioneer pilots and prospective buyers representing museums and aero clubs. Looking at the amazing structures of wood, canvas and wire, Ginger found it hard to believe that these, in their day, had been the queens of the air; that from them, in a lifetime, had been developed the high performance aircraft now annihilating space in every corner of the earth.

In a brief conversation with Sir Giles, to whom Biggles made himself known, they learned that while none of the machines was likely to qualify for a Certificate of Airworthiness, every one had flown, and could still, at any rate, get off the ground. He confirmed that he had flown the Flying Crusader the previous day. "It would be a tragedy to see them go on the scrap heap," he said sadly. "I'm hoping most of them will end their days in museums."

"I suppose you never heard anything more of the Flying Crusader picture that diasppeared?" prompted Biggles. "I've been refreshing my memory from the police files."

"No," answered Sir Giles. "It's gone for good I'm afraid. Like these machines, that unhappy business belongs to history. I named my machine after the picture, of course. I'm afraid poor old Smithers must have gone out of his mind and hidden the picture somewhere for safety. He seemed to have a curious regard for it. The other man in the case, Silberman, went back to the States and I lost touch with him."

"He isn't in the States now," returned Biggles. "I happen to know that the Anti-American Activities Committee are looking for him."

Apparently Sir Giles did not hear, or the significance of what Biggles had said was lost on him, for with a quick "Excuse me, the sale is beginning," he strode off.

In a somewhat depressing atmosphere Biggles and his friends watched aircraft that had made history being knocked down at prices lower than a junk dealer would have paid for old cars. The only brisk bidding was when a film director bought an early Farman to use as a prototype in a film he was making.

"The Crusader's next," muttered Ginger looking at his catalogue.

"Keep your eyes open everybody," reminded Biggles.

Bidding for the Flying Crusader started well, but by the time the one hundred pounds mark had been reached Ginger was alone with a young man who called his offers in an American accent. The keenness of the duel after the previous desultory sales did not fail to attract attention, and as the price rose Biggles noticed an expression of growing embarrassment on the young American's face. Ginger, too, began to look worried when he reached two hundred pounds, and still Biggles had made no sign. Suddenly the American turned away and after a brief pause the auctioneer's hammer fell. The Flying Crusader had been knocked down to Ginger for £220, the highest figure of the day.

"What shall I tell the reporters if they question me?" Ginger asked Biggles.

"Say you represent the Air Ministry, which in a way is true enough," answered Biggles. "You can also let it be known that as the aircraft has petrol in her tank you intend to fly it to its new home to-morrow – you needn't say where."

Ginger looked alarmed. "Fly it? Are you kidding?"

"No. She'll fly. You heard what Sir Giles said?"

"What's the idea?"

"I want to encourage somebody, possibly our young American friend, to make a final effort to get hold of the Crusader before it disappears for good. Meanwhile it can go back into the hangar. I shan't take my eyes off it. We'll take turns to watch. I can see Smithers over there. I want to speak to him. Get the machine under cover and put the car handy behind the hangar in case we need it."

SAFEGUARDING the Flying Crusader turned out to be a long and tiresome vigil, for not until the first grey of dawn showed in the sky beyond the open front of the hangar was there any sign of an intruder. Then a figure, moving silently, showed for a moment silhouetted against the paling stars.

Just as quietly Biggles moved. His torch cut a wedge of light in the gloom revealing the startled face of the young American. Indeed, such was his confusion that it was apparent he was not accustomed to questionable nocturnal practices.

A man was hurrying towards him.

"Are you looking for something?" asked Biggles quietly.

"I – well – I was – er – just having a last look at the old crate," stammered the new arrival.

Biggles' voice hardened. "Funny time to choose. You'll have to give a more convincing explanation than that in court. I'm a police officer."

"Police!" The American looked aghast. "Now wait a minute," he pleaded. "Gimme a chance. I don't want this bundle of sticks on wheels. What would I do with it?"

"That's what I want you to tell me," returned Biggles crisply. "Come on, let's have the truth."

"I wasn't doing any harm."

"You were hoping to take this machine away. Why?"

"Oh, just to make some easy money, I guess," muttered the American in a resigned voice.

"How? Come on, or you can answer questions somewhere else."

"Listen," said the American earnestly. "If you pick me up for this I'm on a spot. I'm no crook."

"What's your name?"

"Galton."

"Where are you from?"

The American shrugged. "Okay. I'll come clean. It wasn't my fault I couldn't buy the kite. I tried. You saw me. I'm a sergeant in the U.S. Air Force in Germany, supposed to be on pass in Berlin. Like a fool I got cleaned out in a gambling joint. There was a guy there named Silberman. He said he'd see me okay."

"Why did he pick on you?"

"I was in uniform. I guess he could see I was a flyer."

"You mean, he wanted you to do some flying for him in return for money?"

"Sure. That's it. All I had to do was come here and buy this old crate."

"Did he say why he wanted it?"

"No. When I asked him he told me to quit asking questions. He gave me three hundred bucks to come over and buy the Crusader. Said that'd be enough. As you know, it wasn't."

"He didn't tell you he was wanted by the Federal Police I'll warrant," said Biggles grimly.

The American started. "What for?"

"Treason."

"The skunk. So that's why he was lying low in the Soviet Sector."

"Never mind calling him names. Didn't it strike you as odd that he didn't come over here himself to buy the machine?"

"Sure it did. He said he couldn't come because he'd an important date in Berlin on the same day."

"What were you to do with the machine when you got it?"

"I was to fly her to a place not far from here – Hookley Green. I suggested Hookley myself because I was stationed hereabouts for two years and know every inch of the country. Hookley was one of our practice landing grounds. There's plenty of room to get down and an old windmill makes a good landmark."

"Is that all?"

"That's all, except he said someone would be at Hookley to take over the machine. He didn't say who, but the guy would pay me when I handed over."

"He was taking a chance, wasn't he, trusting you with three hundred dollars?"

"Not likely," said the American bitterly. "He'd got me where he wanted me if I ratted on him. Oh he's wise, that guy. You see, officially, I'm not allowed out of Berlin. To get me out he gave me forged papers. If I skipped with the money all he had to do was ring up my squadron, and then where would I be with a phoney pass? I must have been crazy to fall for this racket – but then, as I say, I was flat broke."

"When were you to fly the machine to Hookley?"

"Right now. As soon as it got light."

"Very well," said Biggles in a businesslike voice. "Now let's see about getting this thing buttoned up. Silberman is an enemy of your country. Are you going to stick to him or are you coming in with us? I make no promise, but if you work with us I'll do my best to put things right with your commanding officer."

"I'm with you," answered Galton without hesitation. "What do you want me to do?"

"Can you fly the Crusader?"

"Nothing to it. It's kids stuff after some of the crates I've had to handle."

"Then give me an hour's start and fly it to Hookley as arranged. Can I trust you to do that?"

"You bet. I'll do anything if you'll get me out of this jam."

"I'll be at Hookley when you get there," promised Biggles.

As he made his way to the car, at the rear of the hangar, he whistled. A man appeared from the shadows. "It's only Smithers," he told the others. "I told him to be around in case I needed him. He knows Silberman by sight."

Leaving Galton with the Crusader they drove through narrow lanes to the spot where the aircraft was to be landed. It was flat desolate country, and they could see the gaunt arms of the old windmill stark against the sky long before they reached it. In it, Biggles said, he expected Silberman would be waiting. There was nowhere else. He did not drive right up to it but stopped some distance away under cover of a line of willows. From there they went forward cautiously on foot to a point as near the windmill as could be reached without exposing themselves. Touching Biggles on the arm Ginger indicated another car parked close in behind the windmill. Biggles nodded.

A short wait followed. Then the lonely silence was broken by the sound for which they were prepared – the rattle of an early type internal combustion engine. Into sight, flying dangerously low, came the Crusader. With mixed expressions of wonder and anxiety the watchers followed it with their eyes as it skimmed the field. The engine died suddenly. The nose dipped. The wheels touched, bumped, and the aircraft, after bumping a little way, finished on its nose not a score of paces from where they crouched. Galton jumped down, and after a whimsical grin at his gimcrack conveyance, lit a cigarette.

By this time a man had left the windmill and was hurrying towards him.

"Silberman," whispered Smithers.

"So you made it?" cried Silberman delightedly, as he reached his pilot.

"Sure I made it," answered Galton.

Silberman wasted no time in further conversation. With a knife in his hand he climbed into the open cockpit and worked on something too low for the watchers to see, but it appeared to be either the floor or behind the three-ply bulkhead. Presently he stood up, holding in his hand a small roll. He then jumped down, almost into the arms of Biggles, who, taking advantage of the man's preoccupation had moved forward.

Silberman's expression would have been comical had the circumstances been less dramatic.

"Is your name Joseph Silberman?" asked Biggles.

"Yes – why?"

Before the man could have realised fully what was happening handcuffs had snapped on his wrists.

"I'll take that," said Biggles, reaching for the roll and handing it to Smithers who, opening it quickly, cried, "It's the Flying Crusader!"

"I'm Detective Air Inspector Bigglesworth of Scotland Yard," Biggles told his prisoner. "I'm arresting you for stealing this picture from Mancroft Castle on a night in August, 1939. A more serious charge may be preferred later so I must warn you that anything you say may be used as evidence against you."

"Now don't be in a hurry," choked Silberman. "We can fix this between us. There's big money in it. When I was in Moscow I found –"

"Cut it," requested Biggles curtly. "You can tell your story later." To Galton he said: "You'd better get back to Berlin right away. I'll do what I can for you."

The sequel, while remarkable, was not unexpected. The old legend was confirmed. Silberman confessed that he had come across a reference to the picture while, as a history student, he was going through the household accounts of the Tsar of the time it was painted. Following a clue contained in a simple cypher on the back of the picture, a panel was opened in the massive frame in which it had been shipped from Russia. In it was found a fortune in gems, the sale of which enabled Sir Giles to retain his ancient home and buy back the Flying Crusader, a silver replica of which now decorates the mantelpiece at Air Police Headquarters.

The honest Smithers, who had lost his life trying to defend his master's property, was avenged when Silberman went to the scaffold. His son, apart from the satisfaction of having cleared his father's name, did not go unrewarded, and is now a privileged person at Mancroft Castle, where the picture that was the cause of the trouble once more fills the frame from which it was cut.

DID YOU KNOW . . . ?

BY JOHN DYKE

CLIMBING PERCH OF INDIA CAN FLIP FROM THE WATER, CLIMB PALM TREES, AND HAVE EVEN BEEN SEEN MOVING ALONG HOT DUSTY ROADS.

BATS GUIDE THEMSELVES BY RADAR
THEY EMIT A HIGH SUPERSONIC NOTE (INAUDIBLE TO MAN) AND BY ITS ECHO GUIDE THEMSELVES UNERRINGLY. THEY CAN TELL IF AN OBJECT IS FOOD OR NOT: A BAT WILL TURN TOWARDS A PEBBLE THROWN INTO THE AIR BUT WILL NOT TOUCH IT.

THE LUNDY LOCALS
LUNDY, THE ISLAND AT THE MOUTH OF THE BRISTOL CHANNEL, HAS ITS OWN POSTAL SERVICE AND STAMPS, USED TO FRANK MAIL CARRIED TO AND FROM THE NORTH DEVON MAINLAND.

A SHIP IN THREE SECTIONS
BUILT IN THE 1850'S AND CALLED THE "CONNECTOR" IT WAS HINGED TOGETHER IN THREE PARTS, IT WAS THOUGHT THE SHIP MIGHT 'RIDE' THE ROUGH SEAS BETTER!

ELECTRON RADIATION CAUSE OF AURORA BOREALIS
VORTEX BELOW SUN'S SURFACE
SUN SPOT

GALILEO GALILEI (1564-1642) ITALIAN MATHEMATICIAN AND ASTRONOMER, INVENTED THE TELESCOPE, FOR HIS THEORY IN 1633 THAT THE EARTH WAS NOT THE STATIONARY CENTRE OF THE UNIVERSE HE WAS CONFINED IN HIS VILLA AT FLORENCE FOR LIFE. GALILEO NOTED SPOTS ON THE SUN BUT WAS DISBELIEVED.

PROFESSOR BRITTAIN

Explains

ELECTRICITY

"PROFESSOR — CAN YOU TELL US HOW ELECTRICITY WAS DISCOVERED — AND HOW IT IS GENERATED?"

"THAT QUESTION TAKES US BACK MANY YEARS B.C. — PEOPLE OF ANCIENT CIVILISATIONS HAD NOTICED THAT AMBER, WHEN RUBBED WITH SILK HAD STRANGE POWERS & COULD AGITATE DRIED LEAVES, ETC. THEOPHRASTUS, A GREEK, IN 300 B.C. WAS PROBABLY THE FIRST TO STUDY THIS FACT SCIENTIFICALLY. ANYWAY HE MADE THE DISCOVERY THAT A MINERAL CALLED TOURMALINE HAD SIMILAR QUALITIES."

— ARISTOTLE OBSERVED THAT THE 'TORPEDO FISH' COULD BENUMB OTHER FISH WITH AN ELECTRIC SHOCK — BY MERELY TOUCHING THEM — THIS WAS SOON AFTER 300 B.C.

— THERE WERE NO MAJOR DEVELOPMENTS UNTIL — QUEEN ELIZABETH'S DOCTOR, DR. WILLIAM GILBERT, REPEATED THE ANCIENT EXPERIMENTS WITH AMBER. HE THEN SET OUT TO FIND OTHER MATERIALS WHICH, WHEN RUBBED, HAD THIS MYSTERIOUS POWER. HE MADE A LIST OF THEM, AND CALLED THEM 'ELECTRICS' — HE SUSPENDED A NEEDLE ON A PIECE OF SILK, RUBBED THE MATERIALS WITH WHICH HE WAS EXPERIMENTING AND WATCHED WHETHER THE NEEDLE WAS ATTRACTED BY IT, OR NOT.

"WHY DID HE CALL THEM ELECTRICS?"

"HE BASED IT ON THE ANCIENT GREEK NAME FOR AMBER — "ELEKTRON""

THE NEXT IMPORTANT DISCOVERY WAS MADE BY OTTO VON GUERICKE IN THE EARLY PART OF THE 17TH CENTURY. HE POURED SULPHUR INTO A SPHERE OF GLASS, WHEN IT HAD SET SOLID, HE BROKE THE GLASS & MOUNTED THE BALL OF SULPHUR ON A SPINDLE. THIS WAS RAPIDLY ROTATED WHILE HE HELD HIS HANDS ON THE BALL. THE FRICTION MADE THE SULPHUR GLOW IN THE DARK — A FORM OF ELECTRIC LAMP HAD BEEN MADE.

VON GUERICKE MADE ANOTHER IMPORTANT DISCOVERY — HE FOUND THAT WHEN AN OBJECT IS ATTRACTED BY AN ELECTRIFIED BODY, AS SOON AS IT TOUCHES IT, IT IS REPELLED. THIS IS DUE TO THE FACT, THAT IF AN ELECTRIFIED BODY TRIES TO GIVE SOME OF ITS ELECTRICITY TO A NON-ELECTRIFIED BODY, EACH BODY THEN POSSESSES THE SAME KIND OF ELECTRICITY AND IMMEDIATELY REPEL EACH OTHER.

"FOR INSTANCE, IF WE HAVE TWO BALLS MADE OF PITH, ON SILK THREADS & THEN TAKE A FOUNTAIN PEN & RUB IT ON SILK, THEN TOUCH THE BALLS WITH IT — THEY WILL FLY APART, BECAUSE THEY ARE CHARGED WITH THE SAME KIND OF ELECTRICITY."

A SIMPLE EXPERIMENT · PRODUCING POSITIVE & NEGATIVE ELECTRICITY

+ GLASS ROD RUBBED ON SILK PRODUCES:- POSITIVE ELECTRICITY

− SEALING WAX RUBBED ON FLANNEL PRODUCES:- NEGATIVE ELECTRICITY

TEST THIS ON PITH BALLS (SIZE OF PEA) SUSPENDED ON SILK THREADS. CHARGE 1 BALL WITH + & 1 WITH − AND THEY WILL CLING TOGETHER. CHARGE BOTH WITH + OR − AND THEY WILL FLY APART.

SYMNER IS CREDITED WITH FINDING THAT THERE ARE 2 DISTINCT STATES OF ELECTRICITY — POSITIVE & NEGATIVE. AS A RESULT OF HIS EXPERIMENTS, WE KNOW THAT TWO BODIES CHARGED WITH THE SAME TYPE OF ELECTRICITY, REPEL EACH OTHER, WHILST BODIES CHARGED WITH OPPOSITE TYPES ARE ATTRACTED TO EACH OTHER — DIAGRAM SHOWS HOW TO PRODUCE + & − ELECTRICITY BY FRICTION.

SIR ISAAC NEWTON & FRANCIS HAWKSBEE MADE SOME IMPORTANT DISCOVERIES IN THE LATE 17TH CENTURY — BUT IN THE EARLY 18TH CENTURY STEPHEN GRAY MADE THE DISCOVERY THAT CERTAIN SUBSTANCES WHICH COULDN'T PRODUCE ELECTRICITY BY FRICTION, COULD BE MADE TO CONDUCT ELECTRICITY. HERE WE SEE HOW HE ELECTRIFIED A BALL OF IVORY. HE USED A GLASS TUBE CORKED AT BOTH ENDS AND INSERTED IVORY BALL IN CORK - RUBBED GLASS & FOUND THAT THE BALL COULD ATTRACT PIECES OF PAPER — JUST LIKE GLASS COULD.

GRAY SOON ADAPTED HIS DISCOVERIES TO CONDUCTING ELECTRICITY, AND EVENTUALLY SENT A CURRENT A DISTANCE OF NEARLY 900 FEET ON PACKING THREAD SUSPENDED BY SILK THREADS. — LATER A FRENCHMAN, DUFAY, IMPROVED ON THIS.

"SOME YEARS BEFORE THIS — IN THE 17TH CENTURY, A PROFESSOR IN LEYDEN, HOLLAND, MUSSCHENBROEK BY NAME, HAD DISCOVERED THAT A JAR OF WATER COULD BE CHARGED WITH ELECTRICITY

THIS IS HOW IT HAPPENED ~"

MUSSCHENBROEK WAS USING A FRICTION MACHINE, PROBABLY A GLASS CYLINDER, AND HE WAS TRYING TO ELECTRIFY SOME WATER IN A GLASS BOTTLE — WHEN HIS ASSISTANT TRIED TO TAKE THE PIECE OF WIRE FROM THE JAR HE RECEIVED A SHOCK! — AN ELECTRIC SHOCK — AND SO THE LEYDEN JAR WAS BORN.

WE HAVEN'T TIME TO DEAL WITH ALL THE RESEARCH WORK - BUT WE MUST REMEMBER THE FOLLOWING:- ROBERT BOYLE (17TH CENTURY, FOUND THAT AMBER RETAINED ITS PROPERTIES FOR A PERIOD OF TIME. DR. MORRISON (17TH CENTURY) SENT SIGNALS BY ELECTRICITY. HENRY CAVENDISH (18TH CENTURY) FOUND THAT IRON CONDUCTED ELECTRICITY 400,000,000 TIMES BETTER THAN WATER. BENJAMIN FRANKLIN (18TH CENT) PROVED THAT LIGHTNING WAS AN ELECTRICAL FORCE. SIR WM. WATSON (18TH CENTURY, SENT A CURRENT 2 MILES (FROM LEYDEN JAR TO LEYDEN JAR) — AND FOUND THAT THE CHARGE WAS RECEIVED INSTANTANEOUSLY.

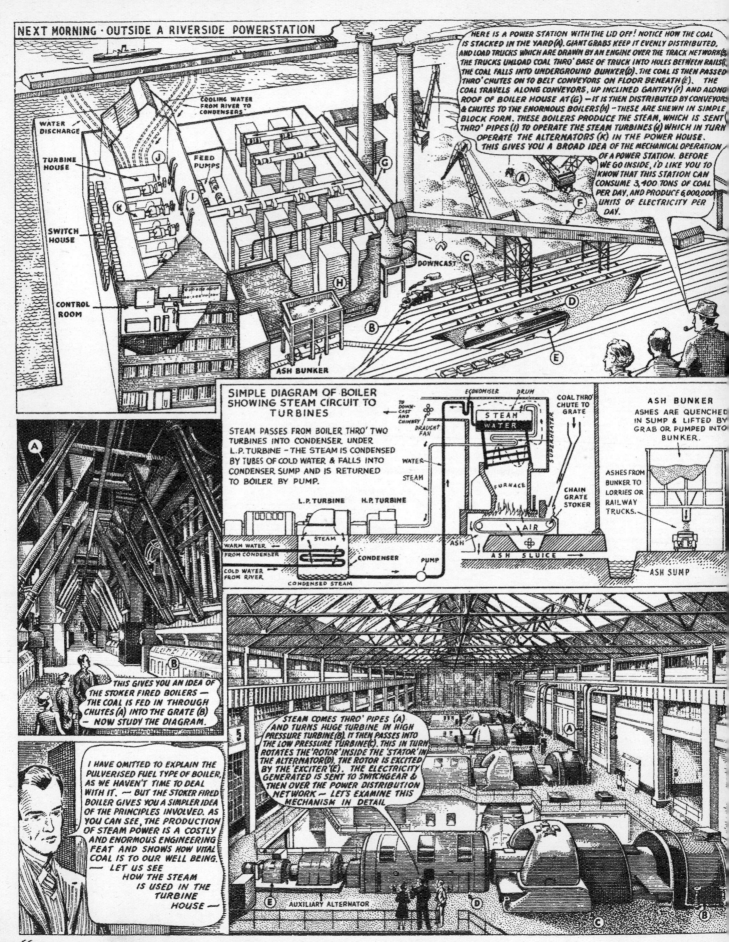

NEXT MORNING · OUTSIDE A RIVERSIDE POWERSTATION

HERE IS A POWER STATION WITH THE LID OFF! NOTICE HOW THE COAL IS STACKED IN THE YARD (A). GIANT GRABS KEEP IT EVENLY DISTRIBUTED, AND LOAD TRUCKS WHICH ARE DRAWN BY AN ENGINE OVER THE TRACK NETWORK (B). THE TRUCKS UNLOAD COAL THRO' BASE OF TRUCK INTO HOLES BETWEEN RAILS, THE COAL FALLS INTO UNDERGROUND BUNKER (D). THE COAL IS THEN PASSED THRO' CHUTES ON TO BELT CONVEYORS ON FLOOR BENEATH (E). THE COAL TRAVELS ALONG CONVEYORS, UP INCLINED GANTRY (F) AND ALONG ROOF OF BOILER HOUSE AT (G) — IT IS THEN DISTRIBUTED BY CONVEYORS & CHUTES TO THE ENORMOUS BOILERS (H) — THESE ARE SHEWN IN SIMPLE BLOCK FORM. THESE BOILERS PRODUCE THE STEAM, WHICH IS SENT THRO' PIPES (I) TO OPERATE THE STEAM TURBINES (J) WHICH IN TURN OPERATE THE ALTERNATORS (K) IN THE POWER HOUSE. THIS GIVES YOU A BROAD IDEA OF THE MECHANICAL OPERATION OF A POWER STATION. BEFORE WE GO INSIDE, I'D LIKE YOU TO KNOW THAT THIS STATION CAN CONSUME 3,400 TONS OF COAL PER DAY, AND PRODUCE 6,000,000 UNITS OF ELECTRICITY PER DAY.

COOLING WATER FROM RIVER TO CONDENSERS

WATER DISCHARGE

TURBINE HOUSE

FEED PUMPS

SWITCH HOUSE

CONTROL ROOM

DOWNCAST

ASH BUNKER

SIMPLE DIAGRAM OF BOILER SHOWING STEAM CIRCUIT TO TURBINES

STEAM PASSES FROM BOILER THRO' TWO TURBINES INTO CONDENSER UNDER L.P. TURBINE — THE STEAM IS CONDENSED BY TUBES OF COLD WATER & FALLS INTO CONDENSER SUMP AND IS RETURNED TO BOILER BY PUMP.

ECONOMISER   DRUM

TO DOWNCAST AND CHIMNEY

DRAUGHT FAN

STEAM
WATER

COAL THRO' CHUTE TO GRATE

WATER

STEAM

FURNACE

CHAIN GRATE STOKER

L.P. TURBINE   H.P. TURBINE

STEAM

WARM WATER FROM CONDENSER

COLD WATER FROM RIVER

CONDENSER

CONDENSED STEAM

PUMP

ASH

AIR

ASH SLUICE

ASH BUNKER

ASHES ARE QUENCHED IN SUMP & LIFTED BY GRAB OR PUMPED INTO BUNKER.

ASHES FROM BUNKER TO LORRIES OR RAILWAY TRUCKS.

ASH SUMP

THIS GIVES YOU AN IDEA OF THE STOKER FIRED BOILERS — THE COAL IS FED IN THROUGH CHUTES (A) INTO THE GRATE (B) — NOW STUDY THE DIAGRAM.

I HAVE OMITTED TO EXPLAIN THE PULVERISED FUEL TYPE OF BOILER, AS WE HAVEN'T TIME TO DEAL WITH IT. — BUT THE STOKER FIRED BOILER GIVES YOU A SIMPLER IDEA OF THE PRINCIPLES INVOLVED. AS YOU CAN SEE, THE PRODUCTION OF STEAM POWER IS A COSTLY AND ENORMOUS ENGINEERING FEAT AND SHOWS HOW VITAL COAL IS TO OUR WELL BEING. — LET US SEE HOW THE STEAM IS USED IN THE TURBINE HOUSE —

STEAM COMES THRO' PIPES (A) AND TURNS HUGE TURBINE IN HIGH PRESSURE TURBINE (B). IT THEN PASSES INTO THE LOW PRESSURE TURBINE (C). THIS IN TURN ROTATES THE 'ROTOR' INSIDE THE 'STATOR' IN THE ALTERNATOR (D), THE ROTOR IS EXCITED BY THE 'EXCITER' (E). THE ELECTRICITY GENERATED IS SENT TO SWITCHGEAR & THEN OVER THE POWER DISTRIBUTION NETWORK — LET'S EXAMINE THIS MECHANISM IN DETAIL

AUXILIARY ALTERNATOR

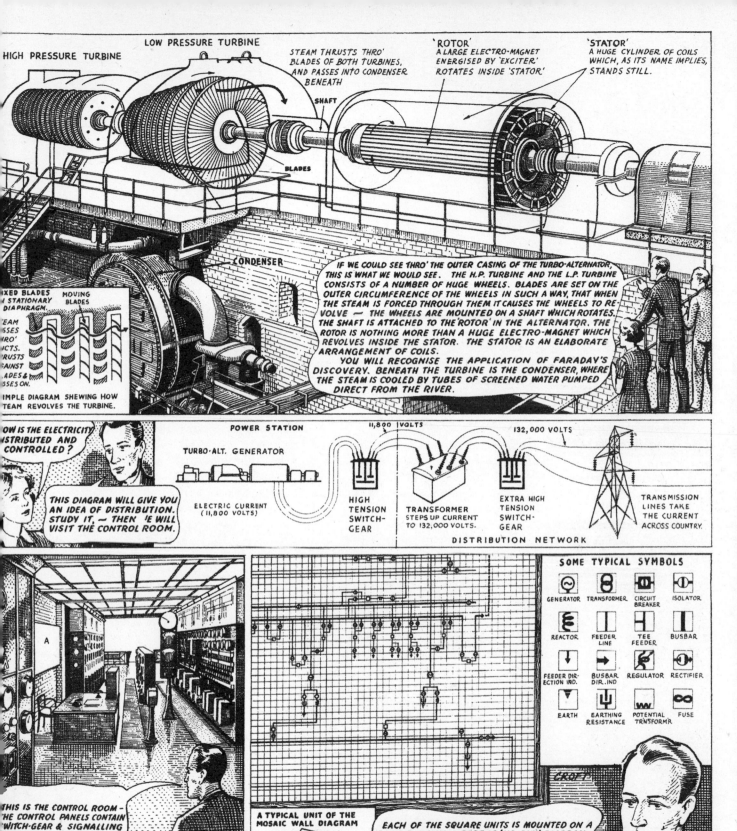

CARIBBEAN SAGA

Thrills of the tough little Island Schooners which brave the twenty-five-foot ocean rollers.

WRITTEN BY RONALD SYME AND ILLUSTRATED BY DAVID COBB

THE Caribbean Sea ? Yes, it doesn't look very large on a map, does it ? Yet to sail right round it is a voyage of 12,000 miles – as far as from England to Australia; and to cross it at its widest part means a trip of some 3,000 miles.

Along its eastern frontier the Caribbean is fringed by a chain of islands which run like giant stepping-stones all the way from Miami to South America. Between each island lie thirty or forty miles of open sea, where sometimes the vast Atlantic Ocean comes tumbling into the Caribbean Sea in fifteen, twenty, or twenty-five foot rollers. It's amongst these islands that one finds the toughest little schooners and the finest seamen in the West Indies.

The island schooners are small craft of thirty, forty or fifty tons. Most of them are built in the little island of Bequia, right amongst the eastern stepping stones. The negro shipwrights saw their planks by hand, shape bottom timbers with a clumsy axe, use a knotted string and a rusty iron bolt as a plumb-line, and buy the few other tools they need in the local ironmonger's store. Yet the boats they build are staunch sea-boats, with fine heavy timber in their hulls, and wonderfully strong (though clumsy) masts. Down in the smelly depths amidship a British diesel engine is installed sometimes, serving to kick the schooner along when the wind fails, or increase her speed when evil weather is coming up over the horizon.

"But I'll sail no auxiliary schooner," Captain 'Royal' King said to me in the island of St. Vincent. "Sails alone are good enough for me. A propeller is a drag on any sailing boat, and I hate the noise and smell of an engine. It's kind of peaceful at night, aboard my *W.6*, when I'm taking her along under the stars and the phosphorescence is gleaming on the sea around us."

"I suppose, even with an auxiliary motor, you run into trouble occasionally ?" I asked him.

Captain King smiled grimly, and asked someone to tell me the story of the 50-ton, two-masted schooner *Laughing Lass* that sailed from this same beautiful and mountainous little island for Barbados, lying 95 miles to the east.

The hurricane season had ended, but the open Atlantic was in an evil mood. Half-way across, the wind rose to a gale. Great seas came rolling westwards, causing the schooner to lift and plunge with terrible violence. About sunset her cargo of 40-gallon oil drums began to shift. They rolled towards the bow, causing the *Laughing Lass's* stern to rise high in the air. The schooner's bow now wallowed almost flush with the leaping sea, and the waves rolled right along her deck. Round about that same time, her engine broke down utterly.

At 9 p.m. the Captain ordered two of his crew and three terrified passengers to launch the one boat the schooner carried. He himself, accompanied by his Mate and four sailors, stayed aboard the schooner in an attempt to handle her through the storm. During the next twenty-four hours, these men worked incessantly at the pump-handle on the deck, drenched and half-drowned by the cold, swirling seas. From time to time they tried to secure the oil drums – a dangerous task with the schooner lurching and pitching incessantly, and the big iron containers rumbling backwards and forwards with every plunge.

The following evening, one of the negro seamen suddenly went mad. Yelling loudly, he flung himself overboard. In the cold twilight, his companions saw his head and arms appear above the surface for a few brief moments. Then a monstrous dark shape with a powerful tail and a nightmare head suddenly rose on the wave-tops and the wretched sailor disappeared. A hammerhead shark had got him.

The Captain and his four companions laboured at the pump for another forty-eight hours and went on trying to stow the oil drums. Every time they managed to secure a few of these containers, a more violent lurch than ever broke the lashings. By this time the schooner's hull was starting to leak from the battering the oil drums were giving it, and it seemed probable that the pump would be unable to keep abreast of the inrush of water. Also, the cask of drinking water was practically empty and the men were beginning to suffer from thirst.

Despairing of saving *Laughing Lass*, the Captain ordered his men to construct a raft with such loose planks and beams as they could find. They hoisted this float over the side and leapt into the sea after it. One by one they climbed aboard the clumsy raft and sat there until dawn, utterly hopeless of rescue.

And with one great bite, that hammerhead took off the Mate's arm and shoulder so that the poor fellow died right beside us on that raft."

The crew and passengers of *Laughing Lass* were wonderfully lucky men. An alert shipping agent in Barbados, alarmed by the schooner's non-appearance, notified the port authorities. A searching Anson 'plane sighted first the drifting raft, then the boat. Staggering under heavy seas, a harbour tug came out from Barbados, picked up the survivors, landed them, and then

Yelling loudly, he flung himself overboard.

At sunrise the Mate suddenly went mad. He hurled himself into the sea and started swimming away from the raft. One plucky seaman, a boy of seventeen at the time, dived in after him and managed to drag him back to the raft.

"And then," this sailor told me, "a great black devil of a hammerhead came streaking up through the depths towards us. Skipper hit him on the head with a bit of a paddle we had aboard, but there wasn't no stopping that brute. He came half on to the raft, so that it canted 'way up in the air, nigh throwing us all into the water.

went back to the derelict schooner. They got a line aboard her and towed her safely into port.

Laughing Lass is still trading between Barbados and St. Vincent, but with a new skipper. Her former Captain never cared to make another voyage after the horrors of those two nights.

So up and down the sea they go, these clumsy little schooners with the tarred hulls and patched white sails. Their holds are full of strange cargoes such as copra, arrowroot, 'bullheads' (heavy roots of banana plants for plantations in other islands), drums of lime-juice, casks of rum, and barrels of molasses expressed from West Indian sugar cane. Every now and then, one of these little vessels fails to arrive. It is a wonder that so few disappear in this manner, for their skippers know little or nothing about the theory of navigation.

Most schooners carry a powerful black pig. The animal is treated extremely well and regarded as a particularly favourite member of the crew, even though he does have to weather storms on deck and find his own shade from the blazing sun. It seems that pigs have a

him on board again with a rope and tackle, and carries on her voyage with much greater confidence. It seems that carrier pigeons and West Indian pigs have something in common!

There are times, however, when even experienced seamanship and familiarity with the Caribbean are not sufficient protection against some unusual kind of danger. The case of the *Dawn*, a big 75-ton schooner, is an example.

Dawn was built in a Nova Scotian shipyard and fitted

The pig is dropped overboard and immediately heads towards the land.

wonderful instinct for knowing in which direction the nearest land lies. In case of shipwreck, the crew follow the pig as he swims through the darkness to some invisible shore, and there are actually cases on record where men have owed their escape from drowning to this valuable guide.

At other times, when sudden rain squalls or stormy nights confuse the skipper as to the whereabouts of some nearby coast, the pig is dropped overboard. He immediately heads towards the land. When his course has been observed, the schooner overtakes him, hoists

with twin diesel engines as well as masts and sails. Under the command of Captain Reg Mitchell, she left the American port of Alabama for Barbados, carrying a heavy cargo of lumber.

Dawn never reached her destination. Aeroplanes and Captain Mitchell's fellow-skippers kept an eye out for her along the course she should have taken during her southward voyage. They neither found nor saw anything.

Three months later, a lonely fisherman on the Mexican coast sighted a drifting vessel a few miles out to sea.

He ran and told the coastguards, who immediately sent out a motor-boat to bring the derelict into port. It was *Dawn*, all right; with her sails neatly furled, her engines in perfect order, and her tanks more than half-full of diesel fuel. Of Captain Mitchell and his eight seamen there was no trace. To this day, none of them has been heard of again.

FINALLY, there is the strange and haunting story of *Island Queen*. It should rank with other great mystery stories of the sea, but this is the first time it has been told in Britain. The Caribbean Sea is 3,000 miles away from London, and much of what goes on out there is seldom reported in London.

On Saturday evening, the 5th August 1944, the fine big 75-ton schooner, *Island Queen*, sailed from the pretty little town of St George's in the Windward Island of Grenada. She was bound for Kingstown in the island of St. Vincent. It was a voyage of about 75 miles. Between Grenada and St. Vincent lie the Grenadines, a chain of tiny and fertile islands, several of which are inhabited. (Bequia, where they build the schooners, is one of them). Thus *Island Queen* would never be out of sight of land during the trip, and seldom more than three or four miles from inhabited shores.

Captain Salhab, an elderly and capable skipper, was in command of the schooner. Aboard her were 75 people; 9 crew and 66 passengers. Most of these passengers were to be the guests at a wedding due to take place in St. Vincent on the following Monday. Amongst them were fifteen young girls, the members of a choir in Grenada, who were to sing during the wedding service.

A smaller schooner, *Providence Mark*, left Grenada about the same time as *Island Queen*. She was left behind, however, for *Island Queen* was equipped with powerful German diesel engines.

About midnight, however, *Island Queen* seemed to slow down a little, for the smaller *Providence Mark* began overhauling her, and finally passed so close to the big schooner that her crew could hear the sounds of singing and guitar-playing, and the young girls chatting and laughing amongst themselves.

The *Providence Mark* sailed on past the Grenadines Islands. At 6.30 a.m. (Sunday), she left the calm and open sea behind her, entered Kingstown Harbour in St. Vincent, and dropped her anchor.

"The *Island Queen*'s coming along behind," her crew told the awaiting friends of the sixty-six passengers. "We passed her during the night. She'd reduced speed a bit, but she should be here any time now."

Island Queen did not arrive that day. People waited for her in vain until sunset. Then, doubting and incredulous, they reported the matter to the police.

Both islands were immediately alerted. Captain 'Royal' King sailed at once in *W*.6 to search for the missing vessel. After him came Captain Curtis Wallace in *Dancing Sunbeam*, Captain 'Whaler' Stevens in *W*.5, Captain George McKenzie in *Seagull*, and other shrewd and experienced schooner captains; men as familiar with the seas round the Grenadines as they were with their own front parlours. At the same time, a high-speed launch fitted with a searchlight left St. George's in Grenada. At dawn next morning, two Anson 'planes roared up from Barbados and proceeded to patrol the sea at a height of only fifty feet above the surface.

It was all in vain. No one ever found *Island Queen*. They didn't even come across any floating wreckage. No bodies were washed ashore, and no oil patches were sighted on the surface of the water. The fine schooner had disappeared, taking with her seventy-five people – many of whom could have swum several miles to the nearest beach.

DON'T ask me to suggest what might have happened. I've absolutely no idea at all, although every time I sailed through the Grenadines I tried to think of a likely solution. Even men like Captain King and Captain Wallace just shrug their shoulders and gaze thoughtfully across the vast expanse of sunlit water.

"The Caribbean's a queer sea," they say. "The American tourists who come down here love to photograph it, and quite a few artists draw nice pictures of it. But we fellows aren't quite so trusting and confident. Too many queer things have happened to most of us when we're away from land in a little schooner."

BARBER: "Your hair wants cutting badly, son."
WILLIE: "No it doesn't. It wants cutting nicely."

Making a

GARDEN

FISHPOND

by John May *with illustrations by* Beryl Sanders

A TRAIL of wet footsteps crossed the road. I drove round the next corner, and in the distance a boy was jog-trotting squelchily along the pavement. He was soaked.

As I caught up I saw it was George, the boy who lives next door to me in the house with a mulberry tree in the garden. "Hi, George!" I called, pulling up to give him a ride. "Been swimming?"

"Fishing," panted George, holding up a jam jar of minnows. "I fell in," he added with a rueful grin. He was in a wonderful mess! Chuckles (and water) oozed out of the pair of us as we sped homewards.

"It's all right for you to laugh," George said as he got out. "Your old car wants a wash anyway. But what's Mother going to say to me?" What she did say, of course, was that George certainly could not keep his fish indoors. "Would *you* like 'em?" George asked me over the back garden fence when he had changed in† dry clothes.

I ought to have been warned then, and firmly said "No". George and his sister Betty are for ever starting new schemes, and somehow I always get mixed up in them. First it was rearing silk worms, then training a puppy dog. And now – though I did not yet realise it – it was going to be making garden ponds.

George thought I might buy a goldfish bowl and keep the fish in that, but the truth is that goldfish bowls are cruel. There is rarely enough surface exposed for the water to absorb sufficient oxygen from the air for the fish to breathe, and the light comes in from all sides – which is torture to fish, because they are used to light only from above.

"What we want, George," I said, "is an old barrel."

There was one at the bottom of my garden, cut in halves. The shrub that was planted in one half had died, so we turned out the earth, and poured in several pailfuls of water to test it. Suddenly dirt shot out of a bunghole in the side, and water poured all over my feet. (George thought *that* was terribly funny, but I did not!) I made a wooden bung to plug the hole, and George nailed two tin patches, one inside and the other outside, to keep it in place. It seemed to hold water now, and George's mother said he could have it in a cool corner of their garden – so long as it did not get smelly.

"Can we put the fish in?" George said eagerly, when it was in position. "Half a mo', though, what about some plants and rushes and things?"

We went down to the brook again, this time by car, with two watercans, a pail, my rubber boots, and a trowel. We came back with a pailful of sand, two or three large pebbles, some water weeds, a bit of root with three or four rushes growing from it, a kingcup root, some watercress, a bit of creeping jenny, and the watercans filled with the kind of water George's fish were used to.

"Tap water might not suit them," I said.

The main thing was the water weed. We emptied away the water that was already in the barrel, and spread the sand over the bottom. Then we planted the weed with the pebbles to hold it in position until it took root. On some bricks in the tub at one side we stood a flower pot with the rushes and the watercress planted in it at what would be water level, and the king-cups and creeping jenny we put into two other flower-pots that stood a bit higher.

Finally, we poured the water in very gently indeed over the bricks so that it did not disturb anything. After a few minutes it cleared. George lowered the jam jar into the water and let the minnows swim out, and the job was finished. We ate our tea watching them, as they darted about exploring their new home.

"They *look* as if they like it," George murmured thoughtfully, and I knew from the way he said it that he was already hatching up a new scheme. After a few days the plants began to sprout, and the little pool looked as

The area we decided on for the pool and its surrounding crazy pavement was about ten feet by eight. Later we sunk it about six inches lower than the surrounding garden, and enjoyed ourselves building a little wall round it three bricks high, with a step on to the lawn in the middle of one long side. The earth was banked up outside the wall on the short sides to make two rockeries.

But before all this, we first dug the hole for the pool itself. It was five feet long and three feet wide. The long sides went straight down about two feet, but the ends descended in shelves, so that we could

YELLOW WATER IRIS

WATERCRESS AND RUSH

KINGCUP AND CREEPING JENNY

OXYGENATING WATER PLANT

FLOWER POTS WITH PLANTS AT DIFFERENT LEVELS

TIN PATCH TO KEEP WOODEN BUNG IN HOLE

PEBBLES TO HOLD PLANTS UNTIL THEY TAKE ROOT

BRICKS

SAND

A simple Tub Aquarium which you can make for yourself and keep in a very small garden or yard

natural as if it had been there for years. George mean-time, as I learned later, was spending all his spare time at the public library, borrowing books about fish ponds and aquariums. And when I saw him again he triumph-antly waved a jam jar at me and called out: "This is what we forgot!"

"Water snails," he announced as I poked my head over the fence to see what he was doing. "Jolly useful chaps; they eat up any rubbish and keep the place clean. The water plants breathe out oxygen for the fish to breathe in; did you know? But what we *really* want is a little fountain."

So *that* was it! George was thinking of fountains. I might have guessed! And of course it was in my garden that we eventually started digging a hole to make a pool which the fountain was to adorn.

have somewhere to put water plants at varying depths.

George did most of the excavation, and I carted away the earth he threw out. Once he called out "I'm coming to coal!" But it was only a layer of black earth beneath the ordinary garden soil. When he had finished dig-ging, I fixed boards about four inches away from the sides, as shutters to make a concrete wall.

"What a lovely game of mud pies!" George said, as we mixed up three parts of builders' sand to one of cement.

We threw in brick and rubble and big stones from the garden to make it go further, and the porridge-like mixture went *flub, blub, slosh*! as we poured it out of a pail down between the earth and the wood. With the concrete set (it took several days), we dragged the boards away, and there was a wall done.

When the two long sides were done, we made the little walls at the ends and stuck old tiles and bits of slate upright in the cement to form a retaining ledge on the shelves. This held the earth which we heaped on the shelves for the plants to grow in, bringing the actual depth to about nine inches and eighteen inches – the levels we wanted.

Finally I got George to dig a foot further down in the middle of the pool, and we filled this hole with half bricks and broken tiles. He was very puzzled at first. But then I cemented it over, with a short length of inch-diameter lead pipe through the cement, and a rubber plug in the pipe – and George's face suddenly brightened.

"I get it," he said, "a soakaway drain, so you can let the water away!"

We also ran a longer, narrower pipe from surface level through the bottom and into the soakaway to act as an overflow. And George had the bright idea of fixing a length of copper wire to the plug, with the end hooked over the edge of the pool.

"So you don't have to dive for it," he explained.

We faced one wall of the pool with pure cement because it looked porous and we thought it might let the water through, and then the job was finished. We were going to fill it with a hose next day, but in the night it rained, and the water drained off the crazy paving (we had laid it with a slight slope, with the joints cemented) and the pool filled on its own.

G EORGE became very impatient at this stage because I would not put the fish in. But the chemicals in the fresh concrete would have killed both fish and plants if we had installed them. Instead, we pulled out the plug after a day or two, let the water away, and then refilled the pool, doing this several times over a month or so until the cement was completely "cured". When the water rose above the top of the overflow pipe, it sucked away with a curious wailing whistle.

"It's that chap we accidentally buried in the soak-away," George joked. "He wants to come out!"

Finally, we let the water stand and mature. It turned brown, then green, and then it cleared. When gnat and mosquito larvae started hatching in it, we knew it was ready. And then one Saturday I came home to find George kneeling at the edge gazing into the water, with an empty jamjar beside him.

"Hullo," he said, grinning up at me. "Caught you some fish this morning. Minnows and sticklebacks. I've put 'em in. They're having a terrific feast off these wrigglers!"

After that, the plants had to go in quickly, because they were really supposed to be there before the fish. We found a flower nursery that was open that afternoon, and brought home half-a-dozen damp bundles wrapped in newspaper. Canadian Water Weed was the main underwater plant to make oxygen for the fish. To decorate the edges we had Marsh Marigolds, Forget-Me-Nots, Bog Arum, Buck Dean and Variegated Rush. We had a muddy time planting them with water above our elbows, but the result looked fine.

"W HAT you want now is a water lily," Betty smiled over the fence.

I made do with some Cape Water Hawthorn, which was a great success. Its white, sweet-smelling blossoms and graceful leaves decorated the pool all through the summer and autumn. And when I bought a couple of small goldfish, I thought the job was complete; the pool looked very picturesque. I might have known, though, that George was not satisfied. He wanted to put in more fish.

"An inch of fish to a gallon of water," he said; "that's the limit. Have you worked out the gallons ? It's 6¼ to every cubic foot. But you *can* have more fish if you want – *if you have a fountain.* Why *don't* you make a fountain ?"

I did not want a fountain. "Too expensive," I objected. But George was tremendously keen, and kept on talking about it. "I'll help you," he said, encouragingly. "It'll look smashing!"

So in the end I gave in.

As we arranged it, the fountain was not very dear after all. We could not run it from the tap without my having to pay an extra water rate, so we set up a big galvanised iron tank on some bricks and arranged for the rainwater pipe from the roof to empty into it. Then I ran a bit of hose along a groove in the crazy paving, covered it with earth so that it did not show, and wired it to a tap in the bottom of the tank.

"That's the water supply laid on," George said. "How are we going to arrange the jet ?"

First we wedged a board across the pool under water, with a hole in the middle of it, and brought the hose up through this. Just for the experiment, we clipped the end of the hose with a clothes peg, and turned the water on. It looked very nice, but the water came out so fast that the tank would have been emptied in no time. Also the piece of wood dislodged itself and floated away to the top. We turned the tap off and scratched our heads.

The final idea was simple. We found a piece of gal-

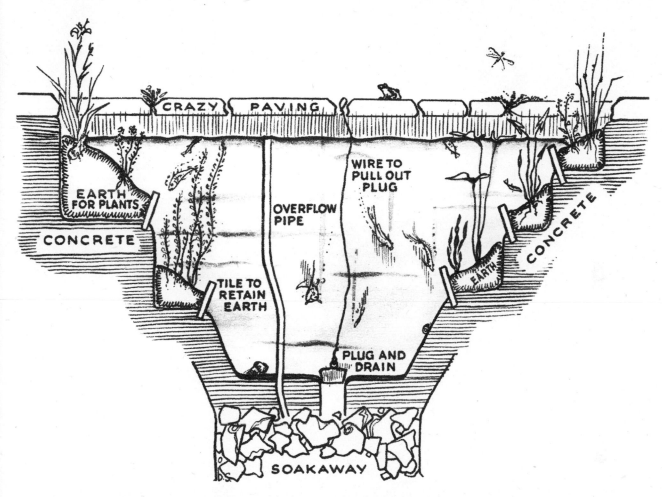

A cross-section of George's garden pool showing his arrangement of water plants and drainage system.

vanised iron water pipe that was just the right length to go diagonally across the pool, resting on the shelves at the end about a foot under water. The hose went down into the water and came up again in the middle of the pool where it was wired to the iron support. As a nozzle we stuck into the end of the hose a very short piece of lead pipe, with the end flattened so that there was just a tiny hole left.

George turned on the water, and a tiny spray about eighteen inches high danced over the pool. The fish loved it. It was extremely beautiful in the sun, and just dusted the surface of the water with shining beads of fine rain. "Like a water fairy!" George exclaimed poetically. He called his mother and Betty, and everybody admired it.

And then, of course, a bit of rubbish from the tank blocked the nozzle, and the spray died to a miserable dribble.

"Blow down it," George suggested.

Like a fool, I did! I knelt beside the pool, applied my mouth to the lead pipe, and puffed heartily. Air started to bubble up in the tank, and then when I stopped blowing, a hearty jet came out suddenly and spurted in my eye! But before George had finished giggling the nozzle blocked again.

This time I did not mean to be caught. "Turn the tap off, George," I said. "I'll open the end a bit with my pocket knife."

I don't think George did it on purpose. The tap was one of those that turns off when you twist it a little way, and turns on again if you twist further. I had opened the lead pipe a bit too much when a great gush of water came through, hit me this time in the neck, and washed my knife out of my hand. I tried to grab it, missed, and fell forwards bodily into the pool.

"George," I said with dignity as I scrambled up, my shirt emptying a torrent of pondwater over my trousers, "if you want a fountain, fix it up over your own tub aquarium. In future mine is going to be just a pool!"

He was too doubled up with laughter to speak. "It was that fringe of green water weed draped round your forehead," he said afterwards. "You looked priceless!"

BEWARE HARPOONS!

A complete story by ROBERT GARLAND *illustrated by* H. TAMBLYN-WATTS

CHOAKA stood in the bows of the *pirogue* with a swivel-headed harpoon poised ready to strike. His black woolley head was erect, his black body, straight and lithe, gleamed in the sun. This was the greatest moment of his young life.

Some distance away there was a disturbance in the water. Choaka was keenly watching the upheaval. Threshing about, rising for a brief instant disappearing on the swell, were a number of turtles.

"Pisez! Pisez! (pull, pull,)" he called in his excitement to the four natives rowing, and the *pirogue* leapt across the water from crest to crest.

The turtles were so engrossed in their dispute that the native canoe was almost alongside before they realised the boat was upon them. There were about six of them. They broke away and flapped unceremoniously in all directions, lumbering through the water like clumsy Noah's Arks.

Choaka watched their humped glistening backs. The oar-like threshing of their flippers made it difficult to see which to follow. Choaka called out at last to the other natives in the boat and pointed to a female turtle making off to the right of them.

The *pirogue* swung round and in a few seconds had gained on the retreating turtle, whose fore-flippers were beating furiously in its attempt to escape. But there was no escape. Choaka let fly with the harpoon and speared the glistening back before the turtle knew what was happening. A series of small bubbles rose to the surface.

This was indeed a great moment! The natives in the canoe laughed and sang their congratulations. Choaka was a man! Eager hands helped to heave the helpless hunch-backed creature aboard. They slung ropes under the protesting flippers, hauled her aboard and turned her over on her back.

Choaka, his white teeth flashing with triumph, stood over his victim. It had been so easy. But the older men of the party were generous in their praise.

"There will be turtle meat tonight," they said. "Choaka's turtle-meat!"

The turtle made no protest now. It lifted its head on its scrawny neck and looked up piteously at Choaka. Glutinous tears dribbled down the corner of its eyes. After some minutes it lowered its head in weary resignation and only feebly showed sign of its resentment for the rest of the trip.

The shell of that turtle would be preserved and polished. It would be Choaka's pride for the rest of his life – his first turtle! He would point it out to his children. "There my children," he would say. "My first turtle! Soon you, too, will hang *your* first turtle-shell for your children to see."

Choaka sat in the prow of the *pirogue* as it skimmed the water – now orange with the sunset. Inshore the deeply under-cut cliffs of dark grey coral cut a sharp line against the twilight. It was broken only occasionally by coarse scrub and coconut palm. After a time Choaka was surprised to find that feeling of pride and triumph had drained away from him, leaving him despondent. Was he disappointed because it had all been too easy? Wouldn't he rather have fought hard for his triumph? He looked at the turtle. Its reptilian horny head lay back on the bottom of the boat, but its glazing eyes still regarded its hunter: not accusingly, but sadly, patiently. Choaka looked quickly away. Many turtles were killed every year. It was not for him to feel sorry for this one.

That night they beached the boat and went turtle-turning. The men waited in the scrub for the female turtles, after laying their eggs, to leave their sandy nests. At high tide the clumsy creatures lumbered back to the sea in hundreds. The natives then ran out and, in pairs, turned the female turtles, leaving them flapping helplessly on their backs. The natives enjoyed the sport, and later they enjoyed the profits.

Y EARS later, when Choaka was first made Manager of that coral isle in the Indian Ocean, he still remembered that day. Was not his first turtle-shell to this day hanging in his hut? And, Dkiji, his son, had he not asked to hunt *his* first turtle? Thinking of that day, Choaka called his men together, and Dkiji stood at his right hand.

"I make a Law." Choaka said briefly.

The men waited, listening.

"No man kills a female turtle."

Choaka knew this was startling news. He waited for it to penetrate the minds of the men. A humming and a murmuring spread through the crowd squatted before him.

"What means this?" "How will we live?" "Knows he what he speaks?" Such questions, at first murmured, rose to a loud cry, demanding a reply.

Dkiji looked up at his father. His eyes held fear. How would his father quell this cry? Choaka raised a hand and stilled the voices.

"I explain my Law," he said. "We live by turtles.

A harpoon quivered at the boy's side.

Turtles are few. Fewer by far than when I was a boy. Male turtles do not come ashore. When we turn turtles, it is only the females who die. But it is the female who gives us the young. We will protect our island from famine. No man shall kill a female turtle lest he die." Choaka said no more. Dkiji listened intently to the wisdom of his father.

The gathering broke up and the natives spread fanwise through the palms.

"Come, Dkiji." Choaka took the boy's hand and they turned to leave the clearing.

With the suddenness of magic a harpoon swung through the air. It pierced the sun-baked soil and quivered at the boy's side. The terrifying spike glinted only six inches from his naked foot. A warning! But Choaka showed no alarm. Swiftly his eagle eye scanned the knot of trees and scrub. If there *was* a shadow gliding away, he could not be sure – the sun plays tricks in the fierce heat of the day. No one else seemed to have witnessed the incident. They were all going about their business, chattering about the New Law.

"There is nothing to fear, Dkiji." Choaka said.

"But, father, it might have killed us!"

"No, son, this is a warning. It says 'go no further'." Choaka wrenched the harpoon from the ground. Then without glancing to right or left, he marched straight to his hut, taking it with him. Choaka called his henchman.

"Kulak," he said. "Seek the owner of this harpoon. Seek diligently and secretly. Let no man know your task."

Kulak studied the harpoon.

"This harpoon," he said slowly, "is like any other. How shall I find its master?"

"But its master is like no other master," Choaka was angry. "Go. Find him."

Kulak went out into the sun. Late that night Kulak ran into Choaka's hut. He held in his hand another harpoon.

"This," he said, "I found at the threshold of your hut."

Kulak spoke quickly. His eyes were round and white.

Choaka took the harpoon. "Kulak," he said sternly, "have you found the master of the first harpoon?"

"No, master," Kulak replied. "I find no master, but I find this harpoon."

"Go from me, Kulak, you speak as a fool. I send you to find the master of one harpoon and you bring me another." But although Choaka spoke in this way, secretly he was disturbed.

The third warning that Choaka had an enemy came the following morning. Choaka sat outside his hut studying the harpoons. Kulak stood behind him, fidgeting. Choaka had not spoken for a long time.

"See, Lord," Kulak ventured. "White man comes seeking to fish in these waters." He pointed to a small launch which was entering the coral reef.

Choaka looked up. "Yes, white man comes. Perhaps not to fish, perhaps to trade. Kulak, we go to meet white men."

ALREADY a fleet of native *pirogues*, like water beetles, were scuttling toward the launch. Overhead booby birds, unable to restrain their curiosity, were diving low over the launch, and the white men in the foreign boat laughed as, for sport, they caught the surprised birds by the legs and let them go again.

Choaka and Dkiji, his son, waited at the water's edge and Kulak went to fetch a boat. While Kulak was away the third harpoon flashed its dangerous warning, biting deep into the sand at Choaka's feet. Once again Choaka could see no sign of its sender from under the palms where the *pirogues* were beached. But Kulak was back shortly and Choaka questioned him closely.

"No, master," Kulak protested. "I alone was at the *pirogues*. I saw no man – no man." he repeated.

"Kulak, I take you for a fool." Choaka said as their boat sped over the water. "But I would rather take you for a fool than a dishonest man."

The white man did indeed desire to fish in the coral lagoons, as Kulak had said. Choaka consented and gave them a *pirogue* and four natives for their pleasure.

"But I make a new Law," he said. "No man kills a female turtle."

The two white men exchanged flashing glances which Choaka could not interpret. It is not easy to understand a foreigner.

"Kulak, my servant, he will go with you," Choaka added. "The tide for fishing is early evening."

As they returned in the boat. Choaka said to Kulak: "The harpoon is the white man's warning?"

Kulak shook his head. "No, Lord, white man not clever with harpoon."

"You will go with the white man, and tonight my words will be remembered."

THAT evening Dkiji, Choaka's son, waited for darkness to fall. He then shouldered a light canoe and ran nimbly up the coral spit that jutted out into the deeps. At his nearest approach Dkiji lowered the boat and paddled smoothly and secretly to the foreign launch. He rested at the seaward side of the bows like a dark shadow. He had not long to wait for shortly the fishing party returned, two *pirogues* full of young turtles. The white men jumped aboard. Dkiji watched from his position at the sharp end of the launch. Hundreds of day-old turtles straight from hatching were hauled up into the foreign boat.

"One franc for each turtle," the white man said.

"Two francs for each female turtle," Kulak bargained. "The new Law makes this necessary."

Dkiji did not wait to hear the calculations. Silently he slipped into the darkness. He was not angry because he had expected what he had heard and seen. He returned to his father's hut.

"Father," he cried. "Kulak is your enemy. Kulak is bargaining with the white man for payment of female turtles." The boy went on to tell Choaka all he had heard and seen.

Angrily taking a knife, Choaka notched the three harpoons with his sign and thrust them at the threshold of Kulak's hut.

"Come, Dkiji, tonight you have proved yourself a loyal son. Together we will punish the white man." Choaka was roused to an unsurpassed anger. Armed each with a knife, he and the boy took the same path down the coral spit that Dkiji had taken earlier that evening. He dared not ask his angry father what he proposed to do.

Swiftly, silently, like slender harpoons, the two brown

Swiftly a harpoon sliced the air as he sped along the coral strand

bodies glided unseen through the water. They left barely a ripple in their wake as they approached the shadow of the launch glimmering on the waterline. Choaka and Dkiji rested under the lee of the bows but, though there was laughter and merriment aft of the launch, no sound came from the forward deck. Choaka raised an arm and nimbly drew himself aboard. Then, lying along the deck close to the gunwales he lowered his arm and heaved his son aboard. Together they lay like palm logs in the scuppers. Through the dimness of the night Choaka could discern the open hatchway, but no sound came from this end of the boat. In the very bows of the launch lay a vast bundle of nets. As Choaka looked, they seemed to breathe. Choaka wriggled forward on his stomach toward them. Yes, just as he thought! Full of newly hatched turtles. He turned and touched Dkiji's arm. This was no time for words. Dkiji must understand.

Choaka tested the bundle of nets. They were heavy with their cargo of turtles. With a deft flash of his knife, Choaka ripped open the nets. Then, almost one by one, they lowered the young turtles into the water. For nearly an hour they worked, setting at liberty hundreds upon hundreds of young turtles, not daring to allow them to splash into the lagoon. With gentle plops, one after another of the tiny creatures disappeared into the dark water. Then, as they worked, they heard the splash of a canoe being paddled furiously. Choaka and Dkiji slid over the far side of the boat, and hid once more in the water.

The canoe came to a clumsy halt, knocking against the side of the bigger boat. The rocking of the canoe against the launch brought cries from within, and a host of feet pattered on deck. Among the confused shouts and chatter Choaka recognised Kulak's voice. He was excited and agitated. He pleaded with the white man to shelter him.

"Choaka will kill me, he will kill me," the servant repeated again and again. "I have seen his sign."

But the white men only scoffed him for a coward. "Have we not paid you well?" they cried. "Be away with you. It is well that you have warned us, for we too must be away. If Choaka has already discovered your deeds, then we must be away this night."

But Kulak cringed, beseeching the hard white man, imploring for his pity. But all he got for his cowardice was a kick and an oath.

"Go, dog, and take your desserts! You have served us well, and we have paid you well. Now leave us be!"

With one final kick, Kulak was thrust overboard, and immediately there was great activity on the launch. The white man was preparing to depart. Choaka and Dkiji who had witnessed the scene awaited their opportunity. Kulak's canoe had gone, and the men on board were scurrying to and fro. Then the two natives slid underwater and swam beneath the surface until they had covered enough distance for darkness to hide them.

Back in their hut there was no sign of Kulak that night. Nor the next day. Kulak was nowhere to be seen. In the brilliance of the morning sun, there stood the three harpoons still erect and shimmering in Kulak's doorway. In his fear and haste, Kulak had not removed them, and the whole village passed by and knew the meaning of that sign. But Kulak was not to be seen.

Two days later, by night, Kulak returned secretly for hunger drove him into the village. But, even as he made his way with false boldness across the clearing, hiding his head in the hollow of his canoe as he carried it on his shoulders, Dkiji espied him. There was no one on the island who walked as Kulak walked, for had he not lost one big toe in a shark-hunt seven years back, which left him lame ? And had he not been the servant of Choaka since Dkiji himself was but a small child ?

Dkiji was so very sure he was not mistaken that he crossed the clearing and awaited the canoe-carrier, for he must pass close by the water-well where the path narrowed. It was dark, very dark, but not too dark for Dkiji's watchful eyes to observe those feet as they passed within a few paces from where he stood behind the well. Yes, indeed, that right foot *was* the foot of Kulak! Dkiji hastened to his father's hut.

"Kulak is in the village!" he hissed. "He is on his way now to his own hut."

Choaka had awaited this very moment. He knew that Kulak must return or perish by the very hand of God himself – perish for want of food and water or perish from some evil thing at sea. Choaka had, therefore, been prepared for this moment. That was why, after Kulak had made the safety of his hut, and was ready to leave it

as secretly as he had come, he found his hut surrounded with men of his own village. Silent sentinels who had once been his friends, now prevented his escape. He was trapped, and as an animal is trapped, he turned wildly back into his hut, and then turned about and hoped to dare the guard which hemmed him in, but there was no escape. Harpoons pointed at him from all sides. He could not escape his own wickedness. Once again he tried to plead and beseech, to cringe and whine, as he had done to the white man, but there was no response. His guard remained immovable and silent. He was a prisoner in his own hut, and there he was to remain throughout that night – a nightmare night for a man who knows he is to die. Morning found him abject and quivering in a corner of his hut. He gibbered foolishly as they approached him to take him to the clearing where Choaka waited to pronounce judgment.

But as Choaka said: "Kulak you must surely die!" the most unbelieveable thing happened. The cringing Kulak turned wild and broke away. How, to this day, none can say, but Kulak outran his guards, outran the mob and sped along the coral strand. But, swifter than Kaluk, a harpoon sliced the air and brought him to the ground. Thus, before the eyes of the whole island, Kulak paid the full penalty of death. Everyone in that village was always to remember, and those three harpoons before the threshold of Kulak's hut served as a warning. Choaka meant what he said, and female turtles are preserved to this day.

CHICKO... By THELWELL

JEFF ARNOLD AND THE ROAD AGENTS

STORY BY CHARLES CHILTON.

YOU SENT FOR ME, SIR?

YES, ARNOLD. GOT A LITTLE JOB FOR YOU!

ROAD AGENTS HAVE BEEN HOLDIN' UP THE BULLION STAGE BETWEEN EL PASO AND SAN ANTONE. IT'S GOTTEN SO BAD NO DRIVER WILL TAKE THE STAGE THROUGH ANY MORE AND THE COMPANY'S APPEALED TO US FOR HELP.

I CAN'T SPARE BUT ONE RANGER, SO I DECIDED YOU WERE THE MAN FOR THE JOB. HOW ABOUT IT?

I'LL DO MY BEST, SIR — IF I CAN TAKE LUKE AND JIM FORSYTHE ALONG WITH ME.

TAKE WHO YOU WANT, BUT SET OUT FOR EL PASO RIGHT AWAY. AND GOOD LUCK.

THANK YOU, SIR. I'LL SEE THAT STAGE GETS THROUGH, EVEN IF I HAVE TO TAKE IT THROUGH MYSELF.

AT EL PASO, ONE WEEK LATER.

GOOD LUCK, ARNOLD. IF YOU CAN GET THAT STAGE THROUGH YOU'RE A BETTER MAN THAN ME.

WELL, WE'LL DO OUR DARNDEST, MARSHAL— YOU CAN DEPEND ON THAT.

GIT UP THERE. HIT THE GRIT!

SO LONG, OLD MAN. YOUR GOLD IS SAFE WITH US.

SO LONG.

THAT'S RED BUTTES AHEAD, LUKE. IF WE'RE GOING TO HAVE ANY TROUBLE ON THIS TRIP THAT'S WHERE WE'LL GET IT, SO KEEP YOUR EYES PEELED.

YOU BET.

GOLDARN IT - THE BANDITS! WHAT DO WE DO? PULL UP?

NO, LUKE. RIDE 'EM DOWN.

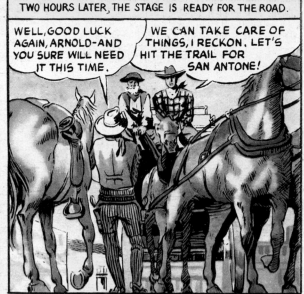

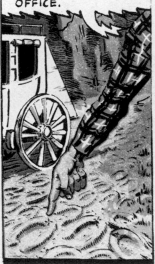

84

Arena of the Brave

The thrilling story of Brooklands

WRITTEN BY DENNIS MAY AND ILLUSTRATED BY GEORGE PYE

OVER and over again, when mechanical crack-ups rob British speed cars of the spoils of victory in classic international races, the same reason is given: "Lack of proper testing facilities".

But what exactly does that mean, you may wonder. Is it just a case of any old excuse being better than none? What sort of testing facilities are needed for Grand Prix races, most of them run over road circuits, a few on airfield perimeter courses? Has Britain always been denied these rather vaguely imagined advantages, or is their absence a purely modern bogey? Do our Continental rivals – the Italians, the French, the Germans – possess ideal proving grounds?

Well, let's take these questions one at a time. To start with, the plea is genuine enough: Britain does indeed lack proper high-speed testing facilities.

Secondly, although the Grands Prix themselves are contested over road or airfield courses, the training for these races, to be effective, demands a *track*, where the highest speeds of which the cars are capable can be maintained for hours at a stretch. It is only by stressing engines and chassis to a degree far exceeding normal race-day standards of punishment that constructors can be sure of achieving cast-iron reliability. A track, it is true, does not test brakes or cornering power, two very important factors in Grand Prix racing, so the 18-carat ideal is a track with a road course standing within the same grounds.

Thirdly, our lack of such a site is indeed a modern bugbear. Before the war we had the legend-studded Brooklands motor course, at Weybridge, in Surrey, about twenty miles from London. In many respects (more of this anon) Brooklands was the finest proving ground in Europe, perhaps in the World even.

Lastly, France and Italy both have very fine testing arenas of their own – on the one hand Montlhéry Autodrome, a few kilometres outside Paris, and on the other the Monza circuit, near Milan. The kernel of the Montlhéry site, which can be likened to a great open-air laboratory, is a pure track or *piste de vitesse*, consisting of two short parallel straights connected by very steeply banked turns of equal radius, supported on tall concrete stanchions. Then, merging into and out of the track proper at suitable points are two "legs" of a tortuous seven-mile road course, which wriggles and twists its way through undulating country dotted with trees and low sandy hills.

Almost perfect for long-duration destruction testing – the *piste de vitesse* measures 2,900 yards per lap and can be traversed at average speeds approaching 150 m.p.h. – Montlhéry is of course easily accessible from Germany, and in fact anywhere in Western Europe. "Invaders" from Britain, on the other hand, have the Channel to cross, with all the expense, time-wastage and formality that that entails for cumbrously-freighted task forces. Small wonder that our racing *equipes* more often fall back upon the greatly inferior facilities offered by airfields like Silverstone, Northamptonshire, where there is no banking and the straights are so short that drivers have to shut off and cram on the brakes before their cars ever reach maximum speed.

Italy's Monza speedway, scene of the annual Italian Grand Prix, is, so to speak, a cross between a track and a road course, and thus enables engines, brakes, steering gears, suspension systems and in fact all of a car's main chassis elements to be tested simultaneously. The principal straight is about a mile and a quarter long and the corners are slightly banked, resulting in a lap speed of over 115 m.p.h. by the fastest cars.

IT is strange and ironical that Britain, which created its great concrete mecca of speed, Brooklands, many years before such a thing was thought of in Continental Europe, should be left trackless in this supersonic age. Nor would it, either, if our generation had bred a man with the combined vision, wealth and public spirit of the late Hugh Locke King, founder of Brooklands.

Brooklands was constructed in 1906 and '07, in the grounds of Mr Locke King's mansion, from which it took his name. In shape it was nearer oval than anything, albeit a rather lopsided oval, with one end curve striking a wider arc than the other. The irregularity of its shape, aggravated by what your geometry master would probably call a re-entrant curve, made real demands on driving skill at almost any lap speed in excess of 100 miles an hour; here, in contrast to Montlhéry and America's great brick and asphalt track at Indianapolis, Indiana – symmetrical courses both – non-stop concentration was vital to safety, and even to survival; it wasn't just a matter of "picking a line", "getting in the groove", and then more or less leaving it to inertia and centrifugal force to hold the car on course – Brooklands called for real muscular effort on the steering wheel, plus never-relaxing nicety of judgment.

These oddities of the Brooklands blueprint were not put in as deliberate sporting hazards. Mr Locke King, although wealthy, had to make the best use he could of the tract of land at his disposal; and this track had its own oddities already built in, the worst of them being the presence of a factory on one flank of the area chosen for the raceway. It was this factory that gave Brooklands its sinister re-entrant curve, that is, a dent where a bulge should be, and, to make matters trickier still, this curve was "blind", with drivers' vision cut down to about twenty yards by the factory's trackside wall.

AWAY on the opposite side of the great oval, just before the longest of the two bankings flattened out to merge into the 150 m.p.h. Railway Straight, the track rose in a gentle hump where it formed a viaduct spanning the River Wey. At the speeds reached in the years just before the second World War, cars weighing as much as two tons were catapulted bodily into the air on this switchback, travelling for four times their own length with eight inches of daylight showing between tyres and concrete. When, as sometimes happened, the surface was awash with rain during races or record attempts, a man's life could depend on his making his landing after such a leap with his front wheels pointing where the car was going.

But, even granting that the big saucer had some quirks and peculiarities that it would have been better without, it was nonetheless a magnificent feat of civil engineering for its day, and proved its creator to be a man of exceptional foresight. In 1907, the year that Brooklands opened, the World's Land Speed Record stood at 121½ miles an hour. Now this Blue Riband of the record book was, is, and always will be set up on a perfectly flat, perfectly straight section of the earth's crust; so, if Mr Locke King had budgeted for an ultimate *lap* speed equal to the then existing Land Speed Record, he could have hardly been accused of short-sightedness. Yet he built a track which, when the last war broke out, had been lapped at 143.44 m.p.h. and, if fate hadn't conspired to ring down the curtain on

One of the best-known landmarks at Brooklands – the bridge spanning the Home Banking.

Brooklands for all time in September of 1939, would undoubtedly have seen the century-and-a-half mark passed ere now.

One lap of Brooklands measured 2.767 miles, the width from verge to verge was 100 feet, and the highest section of banking rose to 28 feet 8 inches. At their steepest points, both the Home and Byfleet Bankings were so steep that you couldn't climb them on foot, even in rubber-soled shoes. Most thrilling of all spectator vantage places was a bridge spanning the Home Banking, from which lofty perch privileged persons could look down perpendicularly into the cockpits of cars roaring beneath at upwards of two miles a minute.

In its thirty-three years of history, Brooklands witnessed the birth and breaking of more speed records, in local, national, international and World's categories, than any other motor course. The first of these, a World's twenty-four hour record, which established beyond doubt the merit and possibilities of Locke King's imaginative project, took place on June 28/29th, 1907, eleven days after the official opening ceremony. Driving a big green Napier car – British, of course – the late S. F. Edge made an average of 65.9 miles an hour, circulating during the night hours in the glare of paraffin flares placed around the lip of the bankings.

A man of action Edge certainly was – he went into athletic training for weeks before his big marathon – but as a prophet he was badly off the beam. In a news-paper interview after his record he predicted "the most appalling accidents" if anyone should attempt to exceed 100 m.p.h. at Brooklands. Yet only a year later, in 1908, Felice Nazarro, the great Italian speed ace, turned a lap at just under 108 m.p.h. And in 1952, in the World's only twenty-four hour *road* race, the Grand Prix of Endurance at Le Mans, France, the winning German Mercedes, with a comfortable saloon body, averaged better than 96 m.p.h. while the hands of the clock went twice round the dial. Thus do yesterday's miracles of speed become today's commonplace.

The story of the Brooklands lap record turns the limelight on many of the greatest speed names of the century. From Nazarro, this coveted "high" passed to the late Kenelm Lee Guinness, whose 350 horse-power Sunbeam went round at over 122 m.p.h. in 1922. With one exception, when the late Ernest Eldridge circled the saucer at 124.33 m.p.h. on a giant Italian F.I.A.T. – the same "Mephistopheles" that had set Nazarro's original mark – the following nine lap records went to the credit of that great Welsh speedman, the late J. G. Parry Thomas. Thomas's best lap speed, before he crashed to his death on the sands at Pendine, South Wales, in an attempt on the Land Speed Record in 1927, was 129.70 m.p.h., all of his dashes being made with a big Leyland-Thomas car of his own design and construction.

After Thomas's tragic passing, battle raged for this most coveted Brooklands honour between Kaye Don, with his "Tiger" Sunbeam, and Sir Henry Birkin, on a Bentley, who was to lose his life from burns received in a racing accident at Tripoli, North Africa.

Then, in the last few years of the Brooklands story, Oliver Bertram and the late John Cobb took the stage. The former, a quiet-voiced lawyer, roared his huge Barnato-Hassan round at 142.60 miles an hour, while Cobb, a London fur-broker of a stature and build to match his even bigger Napier Railton, broke the record three times in all, being the first to top the 140 mark and having the final say with the 143.44 m.p.h. burst mentioned earlier in this article.

In the course of the record that must now stand for all time, Cobb recorded the highest speed ever timed over a measured distance at Brooklands – 151.97 m.p.h. for one kilometre (roughly five-eighths of a mile) in the Railway Straight. Cobb also set the highest race-winning average in Brooklands history – 136.03 m.p.h. in 1937. Merely to maintain such a speed as that for several consecutive laps of this difficult track was a feat, but to do so while weaving through a spread-out field of slower cars and less-skilled drivers demanded prodigious courage and track-craft. Right round both bankings, Cobb rode the very lip of the track, where any split-second mishap, such as a tyre-burst, would inevitably send car and pilot reeling into the fringe of trees and beyond.

Cobb also travelled faster on land than any other man in the world, and before his tragic death in 1952 was the holder of the Land Speed Record – set up in Utah, U.S.A., in 1947 – at 394.19 m.p.h. Mention of his Brooklands car, the single-engined Napier Railton, calls to mind the fantastic contrasts between the largest and the smallest Brooklands machines. At the bottom end of the scale there was a tiny whizzbang called the Jappic, propelled by a single-cylinder motorcycle engine that you could lift with one hand. Then Cobb's Juggernaut, among the largest, but not *the* largest, in that brave company, had an aeroplane engine with a capacity roughly twenty-five times greater than an 8 h.p. Ford. Most gargantuan Brooklands car of all – about thirty times the small Ford's capacity – was the 27-litre Higham Special raced in the early 'twenties by an ace of the day, Count Zborowski.

A NOTICE always displayed at Brooklands, and still displayed at our present-day racing venues, warns the public, MOTOR RACING IS DANGEROUS. Well, it is, and this was a fact that the great Brooklands figures knew and faced. Speed was in their blood, so they cheerfully accepted the game's hazards, partly for the sheer thrill of the thing and partly because they realised that speed was the acid test of an automobile, the test that paved the way to technical developments that would place and keep Britain ahead of her overseas rivals. Thus it wasn't surprising that crashes, some fatal, some not, shadowed almost every phase of the Brooklands epic.

The great dread of all Brooklands drivers was "going over the top" – the top of the banking, that is. How many actually did so, between 1907 and 1939, I couldn't say, but few who made the dive lived to tell the tale. Capt. J. A. Toop was one who ended his career that way. I remember this tragedy particularly because it occurred during the first track meeting I ever attended, when a boy in shorts. Poor Toop's Peugeot was close on the tail of another French car, a Ballot, when it seemed that a gust of wind struck the Peugeot on the Byfleet Banking. It swerved hard to starboard, shot over the edge and disappeared from view. When officials reached the spot, Toop was dead.

Later, in the classic 500-Miles Race of 1932, a rather similar disaster overtook Clive Dunfee, who had just taken over the wheel of a big Bentley from his brother Jack. In attempting to overtake a Bugatti driven by Earl Howe, Dunfee went too high on the Home Banking and leapt the lip, with instantly fatal results. In this case the wrecked car landed in one of the precinct roads carrying spectator traffic, and the only consolation was that no passenger cars were traversing the spot at the time.

AN instance of not one but two speedmen living to tell the tale of the same over-the-top swoop occurred during the 200-Miles Race in 1922. In those days, most track cars had two-seater bodies and carried a mechanic as passenger. The vehicle involved in this wreck was a Talbot-Darracq, driven by a well-known Frenchman, Jean Chassagne, and carrying Paul Dutiot as "ballast". On the Byfleet Banking, at a speed just below 100 m.p.h., one of the Talbot's tyres burst. The car lurched, out of control, towards the rim of the concrete precipice, then hurled itself over to destruction. But, as it vanished, it catapulted Chassagne and Dutiot from their seats, simultaneously tearing both shoes from the driver's feet and depositing them neatly, side by side, on the track. Neither Frenchman was hurt.

A Siamese, Prince Birabongse, who races under the name of B. Bira, and a German, Hans Berg, were the central figures in an equally miraculous escape many years later, in 1938. It happened in the first few seconds of the International Trophy Race, which was run over one of Brooklands' several "artificial" road courses, about which I shall have more to say later.

The first leg of this circuit was rather similar to the cross-bar of the letter "T", and drivers were supposed to swing left down the "T's" perpendicular on reaching the right-angle. Bira, making good use of the colossal acceleration of his big supercharged Maserati, reached the corner first and started to make his turn. Then, out of the tail of his eye, he got a glimpse of a white streak coming up on his left. It was Berg's smaller Maserati. The German, a stranger to Brooklands, had somehow misunderstood the instructions and was making to dash clear across the top of the "T". With all his strength, Bira wrenched at his wheel, but not before the two cars had collided with sickening impact. The tank of Bira's car, mounted just behind his head and filled with twenty gallons of racing alcohol fuel (the so-called "liquid dynamite"), was torn bodily from its mountings, and cut a small gash in his scalp. For a second, flames licked up in the prince's cockpit, then subsided and went out.

Berg didn't suffer so much as a bruise, although his car took heavy punishment, and a few stitches in his head soon put the wiry little Siamese to rights. More than twenty other cars, coming up astern in tight-packed formation, dodged the mêlée by fractions of inches.

It was, I think, in 1926 that it occurred to someone to introduce "synthetic" road racing at Brooklands, to satisfy a need created by the fact that in Britain, unlike Continental countries, the official closing of public highways for real road racing was and still is disallowed by law. A feature of the track was an in-field stretch of concrete forming a chord (in the geometrical sense)

chord, by cutting the main circuit into two, gave opportunities for ingenious ringing of the changes. Further elaborating on the same theme, some race organising clubs, taking advantage of the generous 100-foot width of the fairways, introduced what the French call *chicanes* into the straightaways, that is, curves or zigzags made by erecting barriers of marker barrels or sandbags. Finally, in 1935, a more or less true road course, called the Campbell Circuit in honour of the then holder of the Land Speed Record, the late Sir

The car swerved to starboard, shot over the edge and disappeared.

across the segment comprising the Home Banking, with its two ends emerging into the track perimeter itself. Of the two corners formed at the junctions of the chord – known as the Old Finishing Straight – with the big outer ring, one, a full hairpin turn, was entirely unbanked and the other banked only for the last part of its sweep. Here, then, was the making of a course that, anyway up to a point, reproduced road racing conditions.

As it transpired, not one but several artificial road circuits were designed at Brooklands, because the

Malcom Campbell, was laid down and a new chapter began in the story of Brooklands.

Most of the races at the track were run over short distances, ranging between about six and sixteen miles, but for contrast there were also great marathons like the 200-Miles Race, 500-Miles Race, the Six-Hours, the 1,000-Miles, and the Double-Twelve, most of them staged over one or other of the synthetic road variants.

Longest out-and-out track event – *vitesse pure*, as the French say – was the 500-Miles, run annually from

1929 until 1936. Highest-ever winning speed for this immensely arduous grind was John Cobb's 121.28 m.p.h. on the aero-engined Napier-Railton in 1935, in a drive lasting 4 hours, 28 minutes and 52 seconds. It was during that unforgettable race that a patch of concrete started to crumble on the Home Banking. Cobb's speed being higher than any of his rivals', he was able to steer a course between this jagged, tyre-killing patch and the lip of the banking, but many of the not-quite-so-fast cars unavoidably struck the mantrap every time round, with the result that literally scores of tyres were torn to ribbons during the afternoon, involving their owners in frantic wheel-changes at their pits.

THE Double Twelve, as its name suggests, was a two-part race with each session lasting twelve hours – of daylight. Its organisers, the Junior Car Club (since re-named the British Automobile Racing Club and nowadays responsible for the car races at Goodwood, Sussex) would have liked to run it "all in one piece", just as S. F. Edge in far-off 1907 had kept going at his 24-hour record by day and by night, but the continuous roar of exhausts would have condemned local residents to a sleepless night, so the two-part blueprint was adopted.

One, and only one, of the great marathons at Brooklands, the 1,000-Miles Race of 1932, was won by women drivers, taking turns at the wheel of a big sports Bentley. These heroines were Mrs Elsie Wisdom, wife of a distinguished speedman and motoring writer, and Miss Joan Richmond.

You could fill pages with a catalogue of the famous speed figures, some alas! now dead, others still living, who either served their novitiate or made their names, or both, at Brooklands. Just a few who deserve individual mention in this noble company are the late Sir Malcolm Campbell, who broke the Land Speed Record more times than any man in the World; the late John Cobb, whose land speed record was unsurpassed at the time of his death; the late Sir Henry Segrave, first man in the World to top 200 miles an hour; Lt.-Col. Goldie Gardner, first in the World to pass 200 m.p.h. in a small car; the late C. S. Staniland, famous Schneider Trophy air pilot, ace motorcyclist and the man to whom for all time will stand the record for the fastest Brooklands lap from a "standing start" – 121.77 m.p.h. on his Multi-Union car in 1938; the late J. G. Parry Thomas, two-time breaker of the Land Speed Record; Raymond Mays, perpetual holder of the lap records for the Brooklands Campbell Circuit and the principal synthetic course there (the so-called Mountain Circuit) . . . and so on *ad infinitum.*

In the motorcycling sphere, too, Brooklands was a cradle of greatness. Of all the brave and skilful riders who rose to stardom there, the one who stands right out in my personal estimation was – or rather is – Noel B. Pope. In the last years of Brooklands, a grim duel was waged between the late Eric Fernihough, M.A., and Pope, for the honour of being the first to lap the main circuit at 120 m.p.h. on two wheels, a feat of tremendous hazard. Pope it was who finally topped the elusive two-miles-a-minute average first, not, mark you, with the track to himself, but in the course of a routine race, with the track cluttered up with slower metal. That was in 1935.

Three weeks later, Fernihough answered with a lap at 123.58 m.p.h. (compared to Pope's 120.59), thus becoming one of only two holders of the special 120 m.p.h. badges that were specially struck to commemorate these feats.

Two years later, while attempting the motorcycle Land Speed Record in Hungary, Fernihough crashed to his death at three miles a minute, and it was left to Noel Pope – a sadder but still determined Pope – to have the last say in the matter of the Brooklands motorcycle lap record. This he did less than two months before the shooting started for the second World War, recording 124.51 m.p.h. average for a lap that even brought prickles up on the scalps of veteran racemen among the watchers. Brave man!

Looking back over these pages I've written, I wonder whether perhaps I haven't overplayed the elements of glamour and danger in the long and incomparably eventful story of Brooklands. The glamour, certainly, was there all right, and so, often enough, were the hazards, but the sober fact is that, considering the millions of miles covered by flying wheels at the track in its 33 years of history, fatalities were relatively few. Speeds, true, were obviously 'way above ordinary highway speeds, but, on the other hand, the men and women who raced and tested at the track knew with absolute certainty that they had nothing to fear from jay-walkers, straying dogs, small children, or any of the other sources of ever-present danger on the public roads. It was because they realised that MOTOR RACING IS DANGEROUS, and were constantly keyed up to defeat its dangers, that its perils took comparatively small and infrequent toll.

When, if ever, a new and better Brooklands arises in Britain, the adventurous youth of some generation to come will find a worthy outlet for the urge to speed. More important still, perhaps, the tall-browed boffins behind Britain's Grand Prix cars will know where to go to stage those vital tests to destruction.

HALF A MILE DOWN

A Complete Story of Adventure in the heart of a Coal mine

by ARTHUR CATHERALL with illustrations by HOROWICZ

SOMEWHERE in the half mile of rock, clay, earth and coal which lay between Elbow gallery of the Johnson coal mine and the surface of the earth there had been a subsidence. It did not show on the surface, where a wintry sun was shining on ground slowly clearing of a dusting of hoar frost.

Up there everything was normal. There was steam puffing from the exhaust pipe at the enginehouse as the winding gear brought full tubs of coal to the surface, or sent empty tubs down to the depths below. On the pit-brow, the women were hard at work screening coal, throwing out dirt, sorting the coal into the various grades. They were chatting merrily, for it was Saturday morning, and very soon they would have finished for the weekend. There was no thought of disaster.

In the Elbow, the oldest gallery in the mine, and the one they had never been able to mechanise, there was a stretch where the five inch pit props of good Swedish pine were all beginning to bend and crumple. Hundreds and hundreds of tons of rock were now pressing very heavily on that stretch, and there was no one to notice the danger. The colliery Fireman had checked the point on his rounds, and everything had seemed normal. Now, in the intense darkness, the pit props were bending, groaning slightly under the terrific strain.

Farther down the gallery six men were loading coal into the small pit 'tubs', while a seventh man, Jud Horrocks, was hooking his pony on to a string of tubs ready loaded.

He slapped the pony affectionately on the neck as he said:

"Come on, Moses, one more trip after this, and we're through for the weekend."

Moses, who had started his life running wild in the Welsh hills, leaned into his collar, strained for a moment, and then slowly got the string of tubs moving. The wheels clattered quietly over the dust covered railway lines, and Jud stepped on ahead, humming a tune.

Jud always enjoyed Saturday morning. It was pleasant to contemplate a weekend away from work. In winter, as it was now, there was always a football match in the afternoon, and Jud was a football fan. Until recently, when an accident had put him out of the game, he had been an enthusiastic player.

The shadows leaped and swayed this way and that as his lamp swung. His pony plodded at his heels. The wheels clicked, Jud hummed, and it was like any other of the many thousands of journeys they had made together until they reached the Elbow. Here, where there was a sharp right hand turn in the gallery, Jud suddenly stopped, and looked back.

"Now, what's the matter with you?" he demanded, and lifted his lamp to stare back at his pony. Moses had stopped, and his ears were laid back, while his eyes rolled a little as if he was frightened. "Come on, lad . . . we'll soon have finished."

MOSES whinnied softly, but made no move, and when Jud tried to take him by the bit-ring, to lead him, Moses swung his head swiftly to one side.

"Here, what game is this?" Jud demanded good naturedly, and made another futile grab. "Stop this caper, or I'll belt thee across the jaw."

Moses dodged, and tried to back, but the string of laden waggons prevented that. Jud finally lost patience and cuffed his pony across the side of the head. To his utter amazement, for Moses had been in his charge for three years, and had always been the most docile of creatures, the pony turned like a flash and grabbed his master's arm in his teeth.

"Ow . . .!" Jud pulled away, grabbed his arm, and by

the light of the lamp examined it. The skin had been broken, and blood was welling to the surface. His hand was trembling, and his wrist felt numbed.

"I'll see you don't do that again, owd lad," Jud said grimly, and taking off his belt he swung it. There was a resounding 'slap', Moses whinnied, tried to leap forward, and then leaned his weight into his collar. The string of laden coal waggons creaked, groaned, and then began to move into the Elbow.

Jud swung his belt again viciously, though this time he merely let the pony feel the wind of it, a threat which made Moses dig his hoofs in.

As he did so there was a sudden screeching of shattering pit props, followed by the grinding roar of falling earth and rocks. Jud gave a howl of fear, and flung himself backwards as dust swirled into the air, and the very ground quivered under the shock as hundreds of tons of rocks and debris crunched down into the narrow Elbow gallery.

FOR what seemed hours the clatter and roar went on; the air was thick with swirling clouds of coal dust. Actually it was all over in a matter of minutes. Jud lay on his back, trying to collect his scattered wits. When he had thrown himself backwards with such desperate haste he had knocked his head against one of the laden coal waggons. His lamp had been smashed, and he lay in complete darkness.

From the coal face came shouts, and when Jud was beginning to sit up lights were dancing and bobbing as his six workmates came running.

"Jud . . . Jud . . . where are you? JUD!" Their faces were strained, and ghastly in the light of their helmet lamps. They feared the worst, and heaved sighs of relief when they saw Jud getting slowly to his feet.

"By hooky, another yard or two, Jud, and you'd have had it," one of the man said, shining his lamp on the piled mass of debris which blocked the gallery. "What an escape, eh?"

"Escape," Jud mumbled, feeling gingerly at the lump on the back of his head. "Aye . . . aye, it were a near do."

"Your arm's bleedin', lad," one of the older men said.

"Arm . . . oh, aye." Jud looked at the broken skin, and then he remembered Moses. "Here . . . the pony! What's happened to him?"

"Take it easy, Jud," he was urged. "There's plenty more ponies. There's only one Jud."

"Aye . . . aye, that's right enough," Jud agreed, but added quickly. "Only . . . I wouldn't be here if Moses hadn't stopped me. I thought he were bein' awkward; but he must have known somethin', mebbe heard it

"Eeh, Moses, but for thee I'd be dead as mutton."

coming. He bit me! First time he's ever done that. Aye; he bit me 'cause he didn't want to go on into the Elbow."

"Well, he's all right," one of the others had gone to the foot of the fall, and was kneeling by the side of Moses. "He's got a stone on his leg . . . but there's nowt else wrong wi' him."

Jud stumbled across to his pony. Kneeling by the side of Moses he lifted his head, stroked his glossy cheek, and muttered:

"Eeh, Moses, I owe thee summat. I wish I hadn't belted thee like I did. But for thee I'd be dead as mutton." Then, turning to the others he said: "Here, come and gimme a hand to get him loose. I hope he's not hurt bad."

There was water flowing into the gallery now as they moved the stone and lifted Moses to his feet. One foreleg was held off the ground, and a quick examination by the light of a lamp told its own story. The leg was broken.

"I'll have to splint that," Jud murmured. "Once I . . ."

"I wouldn't bother too much about him, Jud, if I were thee," the oldest man present said. "We'd better be thinkin' about ourselves. Look at this watter. Pourin' in like a flood it is."

"Hm!" Jud looked at the black river pouring from beneath the fall of earth. It was racing down towards the coal face, gurgling, bubbling, racing in at flood speed. "Aye, well, a few minutes won't make much difference, an' I owe Moses somethin' for saving my life."

While the others went to the coal face for picks, shovels, and their coats, Jud found two suitable pieces of broken pit prop, and with these, and strips from his working vest, he strapped the broken foreleg. Moses nuzzled gently at the back of his neck all the time he was working, as if he appreciated what was being done for him.

There was bad news when the others came back from the coal face. The big pipe which brought fresh air to the gallery must have been broken by the fall in the Elbow. No more air was coming in. They were cut off in every way, and even if the water did not drown them, they would not last very long down there, with no fresh air coming in.

"Course, they'll soon be digging for us," someone said nervously. "In the meantime . . . I reckon we might as well be doing a bit for ourselves."

Three of the six lamps were switched-off, to save the batteries, and the men took it in turns to attack the fall of rock. They stopped every few minutes to listen for sounds of someone working on the other side, but several hours had passed before they heard the far-off tap-tap-tap of a pick.

Excitedly they stood and listened while the oldest man there tapped with his pick on a large stone in the fall. Sound carries well through the earth, and they must get news to those on the other side that they were alive. It took the better part of half an hour's patient tapping to get a message from the rescue team, and when that message was translated, the faces of the men grew even graver. The fall covered thirty yards of the Elbow. Ninety feet of rock and rubble lay between them and safety.

"They've got all the men they can crowd in working," the oldest collier said, laying down his pick. "It's just a question of . . . well, whether they can get us before the water does."

They turned to Jud who had been marking the wall, watching the rise of the flood.

"I reckon about ten hours," Jud said soberly, rising to his feet. "Ten hours . . . and if they can dig through ninety feet in that time they'll deserve a gold clock each. Lads . . . they'll never do it."

THOUGH each of the other six felt Jud was right, they refused to give up hope, but kept on working. Six hours later, with the flood water now waist deep, they could hear the continual thud-thud-thud of picks and shovels from the other side of the fall. The rescue team was working hard . . . but the water was still rising.

Two hours later the water was chest deep, and Moses was snuffling uneasily, for the water was up to his head. Jud voiced the fears of the others when he muttered:

"I can't understand what they're doin' on the other side. I can hear the picking clearer . . . but there's only one, or I'm a Dutchman. What's happened to the rest of 'em? Why is there only one working?"

"Maybe they've struck water as well, Jud," the oldest collier suggested. Then, to change the conversation he said: "What about Moses? I think the kindest thing would be to knock him on the head. I can't stand by an' watch him drown by inches."

Jud looked startled.

"Nay, I'll not do that," he said emphatically. "He'll have the same chance as me. If I have to hold his head above water."

He splashed about, collecting stones, and built a foot high platform on which he put Moses' front hoofs. That lifted the pony's head higher, but the water was rising steadily all the time.

The men had ceased talking. They could no longer work at the fall. They were weary, shivering from cold, and in no fit state to wield either pick or shovel. Each was listening to the thud-thud-thud of a single pick, then a scuffling sound, then the scrape of a shovel . . . but all the time it was obvious only one man was working.

THEN, so suddenly that the entombed miners were too startled for a few moments to move, there was a clatter and a splash. Then the light of their single lamp shone on the bright point of a pick. The rescuers had broken through.

Husky yells of delight as the men splashed through to help widen the breach. Then they stood and stared at the head of a black-faced, very weary collier.

"Listen, lads," he said when assured that all seven men were safe. "We've made a little tunnel . . . just big enough to get through. You'd best follow me as quick as you can. There's water everywhere . . . and there's no telling how long this bit of a tunnel will hold up." With that he began to worm his way backwards, leaving a hole some fifteen or sixteen inches in diameter to show where he had been.

The youngest man there turned to the oldest, and with a forced grin said:

"Come on, dad . . . age before beauty. You go first."

The oldest man was helped into the hole, and he began to worm and wriggle his way to safety. The second oldest followed, while the other five stood and watched. They knew enough about tunnelling to realise that if that tiny tunnel did collapse there would be no second chance for anyone who was left.

With five of them out it was Jud's turn.

"Don't dally, Jud," the youngest miner said. "I don't want to miss my Sunday morning egg an' bacon. Once you are through . . . I'll be after you like a whippet after a rabbit."

Jud turned and looked at Moses. Once again the water was lapping the pony's cheeks. Moses was having to hold his head up to breathe. A half hour, forty minutes at the most, and Moses would drown.

"You go," Jud said huskily. "I . . . I'll hang on a minute with the pony. It . . . oh, lor, it don't seem right to leave him like this."

"Come on, Jud, get going," his companion urged. "You can't get him out, so you might as well get going."

"You go," Jud said, "I'll see if I can get him a bit higher. Mebbe somethin' will happen. Go on. . . I'll not be a minute."

His companion scrambled into the hole, out of which water was now gurgling in a black stream. Just for a moment the collier's legs and feet were visible as he shuffled his way towards safety. Then there was only the black aperture.

A last pat, a soft whinny from Moses, and Jud turned to the escape tunnel.

A sudden rush of water from the escape tunnel drove Jud back, and then there was no escape tunnel. It had fallen in, collapsing gently until there was no sign that a tunnel had ever existed.

Jud stared. He swallowed jerkily. Had he not stayed to give a last word of comfort to his pony, he would have been in that tunnel when it collapsed. He would have been trapped, probably crushed to death at this very

"He'll have the same chance as me, if I have to hold his head above water."

Jud was already working for his pony. He built up the platform a few more inches, and Moses was once more head above water. The pony whinnied softly, and there was agony in Jud's voice as he stood for a moment and held the wet head against his own face.

"I'm sorry, owd lad," he whispered, "if I could do anything else I would . . . but I'll have to leave thee, now. If I don't . . . there'll be two of us to die. I . . ." He could say no more. Jud was tough, as miners must be, but he was near to crying now at the thought of leaving his pony to die alone.

moment. Cold though he was beads of perspiration broke out on his forehead at the thought.

Licking his coal blackened lips he turned back to Moses. The pony was watching him, its eyes shining in the light of the single lamp suspended from a roof timber. Moses nickered, and the sound seemed to be magnified in the quietness of the flooded gallery. The water was no longer chuckling and gurgling, for it was flooding in from below the surface. The gallery was strangely silent until Jud splashed back to his pony's side.

"Well," he said huskily, stroking Moses's wet cheek,

"I reckon that's twice you've saved me today. It's gettin' a bit of a habit. If we . . . get out of here . . . I'll see you get a medal . . . aye, a gold medal."

For twenty minutes after that they stood together in silence, each giving the other courage. The water was rising remorselessly, an enemy against which they had no weapon at all. It reached Jud's neck, and poor Moses, who had been standing on the little stone platform Jud had built, was rolling his eyes in fear.

Jud began to comfort him.

"Now, don't fret, Moses," he whispered. "They're workin' on the other side for us. Its just a matter of hanging on. That's all we've got to do . . . hang on. See what I mean . . . hang on till they break through to us."

He knew it was nonsense, for now there was not even the sound of a pick or a shovel. The rescue team had been defeated. Six had been got out, but there was no hope for the seventh.

Jud began to pray, and he had just said 'Amen', when deep behind the barrier of rock and debris there was a faint, dull boom. It started the lamp shivering, and made tiny waves quiver across the black surface of the flood water.

Moses whinnied. Jud held his pony more tightly, wondering. Then it seemed as if the whole world began to move. The barrier of rocks and debris which sealed them in the mine began to crumple, as if a giant hand was drawing it away. The water surged after it. Jud was swept off his feet. Moses was plucked from his perch and almost fell as he tried to keep his injured right foreleg off the ground.

Then the rush of water increased. On the far side of the fall the rescue team had tried a desperate, last minute attempt to break through. They had tried firing a dozen 'shots' of explosives, and it had worked. Water had been pouring through the fall, weakening it, and the pent-up flood in the Elbow did its share nobly. Rocks, earth, smashed pit props, were all pushed along, breaking up as they went.

Jud never knew what took place in the next few minutes. He was conscious of struggling against the pull of the flood. Of being on his knees, then face down while water plucked at him with irresistible force. Then his head hit something, and he saw a million stars before falling into a well of blackness deeper than anything he had ever known before.

When he struggled back to consciousness he was aware of a sharp pain in his shoulder. He could see nothing at all. He tried to turn. The pain increased, and then as he swore the pain stopped, and he fell on to his face in six inches of mud and slime. Then, and not till then, did he realise the pain was from the teeth of Moses. The pony had been holding him out of the mud. But for Moses he must have drowned.

He was still fondling the pony, and talking to it when the rescue party fought their way to him three quarters of an hour later.

The Vet talked of shooting the pony to put him out of his misery, but Jud stopped that. His language to the Vet was not ordinary Queen's English, but it did impress the Veterinary surgeon, and Moses was saved.

There is a new pony in the Elbow gallery now. Moses has been pensioned off by the National Coal Board. He walks his pasture with a limp, and around his neck, by a metal chain there hangs a medal. It is a queer medal for a pony to wear, for the inscription reads: 'Cowen District Football League. Season 1950-51. Jud Horrocks (Full back) Powerfield Rovers'. It is a gold medal, and the pitmen who stop now and then to feed crusts, biscuits, and sweets to Moses often read the inscription and smile. Half a mile down in the Elbow Gallery old Moses was more than a full-back – he had been the last line of defence for Jud, and a life saver.

TEACHER: "Many great men in history rose by their own efforts."
TOMMY: "I suppose, sir, that was before alarm clocks were invented?"

DID you hear about the schoolboy who described a Jack-in-the-Box as a sailor giving evidence in a police court?

Kites and Kite Flying

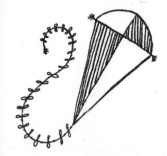

There is more to this simple pastime

than most people think

BY A. M. COLBRIDGE

YOU may often have admired the smooth, steady flying of well-designed, well-balanced kites and possibly wondered what is the secret behind their success. Actually there is no special secret. Kite designing and kite flying is really quite simple, once you know the basic principles which govern how a kite will perform.

A kite is really a flat plate tethered to a string or line and supported in the air in a very similar manner to the wings of an aeroplane supporting that aeroplane in flight. The main difference is that the kite stands still and the wind blows past it, while the aeroplane moves forward and creates its own 'wind' blowing past the wings. In both cases the air blowing past the supporting surfaces (the kite or the wings) produces an upward or 'lift' force and so supports the weight. Fig. 1.

Now the amount of 'lift' produced will vary with the speed of the wind and also the angle at which the 'lifting surface' is inclined to the wind. It will, of course, also vary with the *area* of the surface. The bigger the surface the more lift it will produce.

As far as a kite is concerned, it must ride at such an angle that the 'lift' force produced is greater than the weight of the kite. The difference between the two you feel is the pull of the line. This is quite simple to arrange with almost any shape of kite, by so adjusting the kite lines or bridle that the surface is held at just the right angle and then adjusting the *area* of the kite to suit the weight. What is not so simple, however, is to arrange that the kite *continues* to ride the air at this altitude and does not dive or zoom or fall off to one side. In technical language this means that the kite must also be *stable*.

Now some shapes of kite are stable and others are not. Quite a lot of unstable shapes *can* be made stable by fitting them with a tail, whilst proper trimming of

the kite by altering the bridle lines can also turn an unstable kite into a stable one.

The best way of understanding this is to look at the various types of kites and see what proportions are necessary for successful flying. It is quite a simple matter to make up a number of kites of different type and try them out. They need not cost very much for most of the materials required can be obtained for a shilling or so. And kite flying itself can be grand fun.

First we will discuss the types of kites which require no tail – the 'stable' kites mentioned above. The simplest of these is the *Eddy Kite*, which is also a very fine flyer. All the best *Eddy Kites*, however, are rather on the large size. They should not be made smaller than three feet long and about the best size is six feet long.

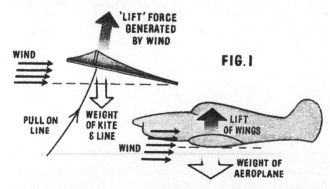

The framework of an *Eddy Kite* is shown in Fig. 2. The two wooden members should be of tough but light wood, like birch or spruce. The shorter member is bound across the longer one at right angles to it, one-fifth of the length of this member from the front. The two tips of the cross member are then joined by a length of cord which is pulled taut to bow the cross member up into a 'dihedral'. Each tip should be raised an equal amount, as shown in the drawing.

The outline of the kite is then formed by string, which can be drawn and glued into notches in the ends of the wooden members. Fig. 3 then shows how covering is attached – almost any light 'windproof' material being suitable. Paper is cheapest, of course, but will tear easily. Material would be better. Paper is turned over and glued in place; material would be sewn in place. In both cases the covering is also attached to the frame.

it will not fly steadily and so it should balance level when supported at each end of the main member. If one side is heavier than the other, add weight to the end of the cross member on the lighter side, such as pins, small nails, etc., pushed into the wood. In the fore and aft direction the kite should also balance level when supported one-third of its length back from the front. Add weight to the central member, as necessary, to achieve this correct balance.

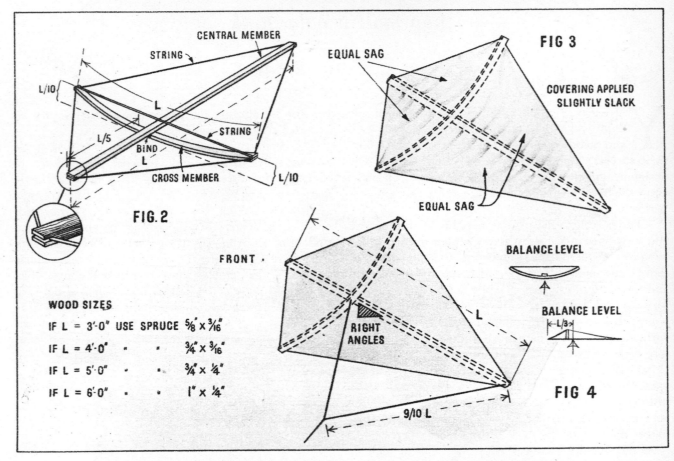

WOOD SIZES

IF L = 3'-0" USE SPRUCE ⅝" × 3⁄16"
IF L = 4'-0" " " ¾" × 3⁄16"
IF L = 5'-0" " " ¾" × ¼"
IF L = 6'-0" " " 1" × ¼"

The four panels of the finished kite should each have an equal amount of sag or slack. This is important if the kite is to be properly balanced. Balance is very important, for there is no tail and the bridle attachment is just a simple 'V' of line – Fig. 4. The main line attaches to the joining point of the two spars, whilst the other line attaches to the extreme rear end of the central spar. This second line is nine-tenths of the length of the kite and should be tied to the main line at such a point that the main line is exactly at right angles to the kite when the bridle is taut. The diagram shows this clearly.

Now for correct balance, which is also shown in Fig. 4. If the kite is heavier on one side than the other

With your kite now properly balanced, the bridle properly adjusted so that the main line is at right angles to the central member, and equal slack in each panel of the covering, your *Eddy Kite* should fly perfectly. If it tips to one side, then almost certainly the fault will be that the covering is tighter on one panel than the other. If it will not ride steadily, check the fore and aft balance again.

If you want a smaller model, then the *Box Kite* is just about the ideal. Main details are summarised in Fig. 5, together with a list of suitable materials and spar sizes. One particular advantage of the Box Kite is that it can be made in very tiny sizes and still fly successfully. Models as small as two to three inches in length, with spars of $\frac{1}{16}$ square balsa and tissue paper panels can reach a height of several hundred feet on a cotton line.

Note that in the case of the Box Kite only a single line is used, this being tied to one spar just behind the front covered panel or cell. The kite, in other words, flies 'on edge', as it were.

A more scientific version of the box kite is the *Rectangular Box*, shown in Fig. 6, which does have a

siderable and we do not recommend our readers to try similar experiments!

Box Kites are amongst the simplest to trim and fly and make an excellent first model since they are quite easy to build. Using balsa and tissue construction, the greatest cost in making a twelve or eighteen inch kite will be that of a reel of cotton or thread for the line. The main point to watch is to make sure that the individual 'cells' of the finished kite are truly square and

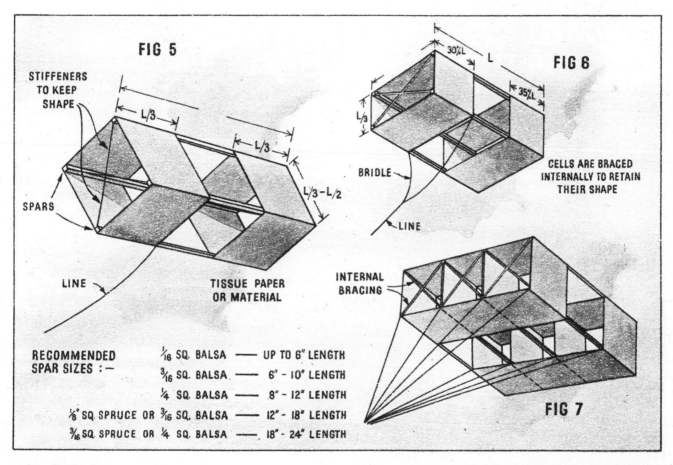

FIG 5

STIFFENERS TO KEEP SHAPE

L/3
L/3
L/3-L/2

SPARS

LINE

TISSUE PAPER OR MATERIAL

FIG 6

30%L
L
35%L
L/3

BRIDLE

LINE

CELLS ARE BRACED INTERNALLY TO RETAIN THEIR SHAPE

INTERNAL BRACING

FIG 7

RECOMMENDED SPAR SIZES :—

$\frac{1}{16}$ SQ. BALSA	——	UP TO 6" LENGTH
$\frac{3}{16}$ SQ. BALSA	——	6" - 10" LENGTH
$\frac{1}{4}$ SQ. BALSA	——	8" - 12" LENGTH
$\frac{1}{8}$" SQ. SPRUCE OR $\frac{3}{16}$ SQ. BALSA	——	12" - 18" LENGTH
$\frac{3}{16}$ SQ. SPRUCE OR $\frac{1}{4}$ SQ. BALSA	——	18" - 24" LENGTH

bridle and flies 'flat'. This has a greater effective lifting surface and so can rise to greater heights. If, for example, you have a simple box kite and a rectangular box kite of roughly the same size and weight, the rectangular box will reach a greater height in any given wind; or fly successfully in a lighter wind.

If you wish, you can go even farther than the rectangular box type by making what is virtually two or more simple box kites joined together. This is called the *Multi-cellular Box Kite* – Fig. 7. These have even greater lifting power and have been used for all sorts of scientific experiments, including carrying a human being to a height for aerial observation. Needless to say the size of a man-lifting kite of this type is quite con-

rigidly braced and that the whole kite is as light as possible. Do not use heavy covering materials on kites of this type.

Now we come on to the types of kites which need tails. The simplest of these is the *Bow Kite* – Fig. 8 – which is one of the earliest kite forms and at one time was the most popular type. Again it is quite easy to make. The frame consists of a central member with a 'bow' of lighter, flexible wood – the same length as the main member – tied to the front of the main stick and then curved round into a semi-circular shape. The 'bow' is held to this shape by a length of string or line between its ends. The remainder of the outline of the kite is formed by string between the

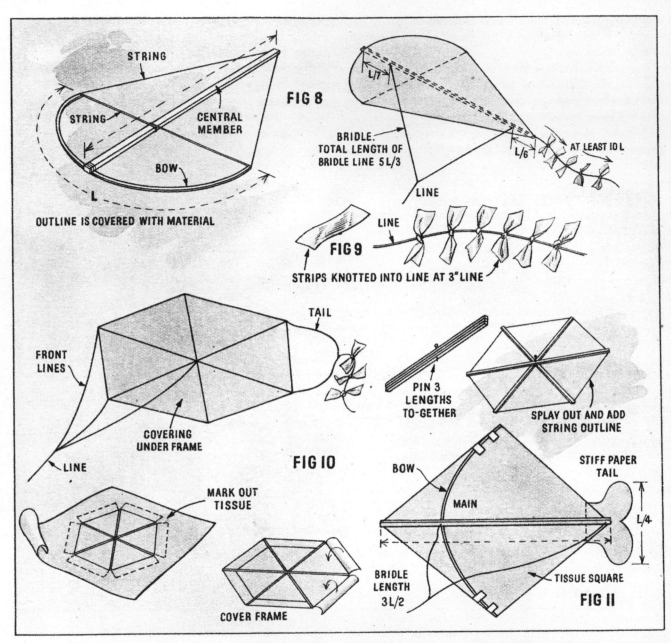

FIG 8

STRING

STRING

CENTRAL MEMBER

BOW

L

OUTLINE IS COVERED WITH MATERIAL

L/7

BRIDLE. TOTAL LENGTH OF BRIDLE LINE 5 L/3

LINE

L/6

AT LEAST 10 L

LINE

FIG 9

STRIPS KNOTTED INTO LINE AT 3" LINE

TAIL

FRONT LINES

COVERING UNDER FRAME

LINE

FIG 10

PIN 3 LENGTHS TO-GETHER

SPLAY OUT AND ADD STRING OUTLINE

MARK OUT TISSUE

COVER FRAME

BOW

MAIN

BRIDLE LENGTH 3L/2

STIFF PAPER TAIL

L/4

TISSUE SQUARE

FIG 11

tips of the bow and the rear end of the central stick.

Covering should be applied quite taut, and to the underside of the frame. The bridle is then attached to the frame, arranged that the front of the kite is inclined upwards at an angle of about fifteen degrees with the bridle strings taut. Since this bridle is attached only to the central member, sideways balance is very important, just as it was with the Eddy Kite. Make sure, therefore, that the kite will balance level when supported at each end of the central stick, adding weight to the lighter side, if necessary.

Now this kite will be unstable without a tail and for best performance this tail wants to be at least ten times as long as the kite itself. There is no difficulty about making a kite tail. Simply cut up a number of strips of tissue paper or very thin material into rectangles roughly six inches by two inches and tie into a length of line, as shown in Fig. 9.

Bow kites, at times, can be troublesome and about the best type of 'tailed' kite for flying for fun is the *Hexagonal Kite* shown in Fig. 10. It may look a little complicated to make, but it is actually quite easy to construct. Simply take three equal lengths of wood and pin them together through their exact centre. Splay out equally and then attach an outline of thread or kite line. Lay this completed frame over a piece of tissue paper, mark out the shape required and cut with scissors. Cover the frame by glueing the overlapping pieces of tissue and folding them over the outline.

Details of the bridle attachment and the tail are given on the diagram. The two front lines must be exactly equal in length to prevent the kite tipping over to one side. To trim the kite for flying, simply lengthen or shorten the third central line to alter the attitude of the kite. Start with the bridle arranged so that the front of the kite is normally tipped about twenty degrees *down* with all three bridle lines taut. If the kite does not 'lift' properly, decrease this angle. If it is too lively and swoops about the sky, increase this angle. In the latter case, however, check first that the tail is powerful enough. This should be at least five times the length of the kite, and preferably longer.

Best size for a hexagonal kite is about ten to fifteen inches spar length. This is an economical size to make and also one which is easy to carry about. If you want a much larger kite, then try either the Eddy or Bow type.

There is just one other main type of kite – the so-called *Indian Kite*, shown in Fig. 11. This is something like a cross between a Bow kite and an Eddy kite, but considerably smaller in size. It has a very small rigid rail and borders between being a 'stable' and an 'unstable' kite. For this reason it is tricky to fly and is certainly not recommended for a first model.

The *Indian Kite* is really a form of aerobatic kite which can be manoeuvred around the sky. Having mastered the basic art of kite flying, a lively kite of this type which will 'stunt' is an added attraction. Kites of this and similar types have been used for 'fighting' and 'string cutting' and similar sporting contests which are possible with kites. They need considerable practice in flying to master the technique of making them manoeuvre exactly as required, but when demonstrated by an expert are particularly exciting to watch.

Successful *Indian Kites* are generally about fifteen to twenty-two inches square. The outline is, in fact, simply a square of tissue of this size. The main member of light wood is glued diagonally across the tissue and a light, springy bow also glued in place, the ends of the bow being attached to the tissue with glued paper straps. The small rail is cut from stiff paper and glued to the tissue covering. By bending the tail slightly the kite may be trimmed to carry out various manoeuvres, in conjunction with the control you have by the pull and direction of the line.

The simple bridle attachment is proportioned to hold the front of the kite about ten degrees down and to get best results it may be necessary to alter the front attachment point, as well as the angle of this bridle. If the kite persistently dips to one side, then almost certainly the balance is incorrect and this should be checked. Otherwise it is up to you to make small alterations in the position and length of the bridle to get the results required.

Now whilst this covers the main types of kites, you may have seen what appear to be quite different arrangements. If you look closely, however, you will usually find that they are basically a Bow or an Eddy kite with, perhaps, an added triangular keel beneath the kite. Quite a number of 'bird' kites are really modified forms of Indian kites, and so on. You can try some of these variations out for yourself, if you wish, but first we would strongly recommend you to make a number of kites of the various basic types and find out how these behave under different conditions. Small kites are best for light winds – box kites or the hexagonal kite. Larger, heavier kites are best for strong winds – sturdily built box kites again, or the eddy kite. To get the most out of kite flying you need to have the right type of kite to fly under the prevailing conditions. And a week's pocket money would probably be ample for making up quite a number of different models!

KEEPER: "Hey, you can't fish here. Didn't you see that notice marked PRIVATE?"
YOUNG ANGLER: "Yes, sir, but I wouldn't be so rude as to read a private notice."

McGUIRE'S GHOST

A complete story by FRANK CRISP, illustrated by WILL NICKLESS

THAT frightening business over McGuire started one perfect morning as we chugged northwards up the coast into the entrance of Blackbirder Channel. Here the green of the Queensland jungle slipped right down to the seashore within five or six hundred yards of our motor lugger, the *Williwai*, one of the pearling fleet that fished out of Doolan on the east Australian coast, far up on Cape York.

I was at the tiller when I glanced over the port quarter and saw the shark. I wouldn't have looked twice at an ordinary shark. We had thousands of them amongst the reefs – ground sharks, nurse sharks, tiger sharks, hammerheads – but this great creature was a queer leaden hue on its back and putty white elsewhere. It swam with unusual purpose, quite unlike the sluggish manner of most others.

"That's a White Pointer," Uncle Scully said as he got his eye on it. "I wouldn't put me toe in the sea within a cable's length o' that beast."

"Ah, they're all the same them sharks," McGuire spoke up. "All scared of a few air bubbles, bigger cowards than desert dingoes!" Dan McGuire was our diver. He was six feet tall, strong as a horse, and always full of jokes.

"Aye, I've heard that tale before," Uncle Scully answered. "One o' them big sharks is like an old bull, ye can scare him off ninety-nine times out of a hundred, but the hundredth time, by dam' he'll go for ye!"

My uncle was a little dried-up man, inclined to be a bit weepy at times because he'd lost his nerve, years and years ago, while diving in Kellway Sound, thirty-five fathoms deep. He was more than ever irritable just now because we were having a very thin time of it. Besides, he never liked the pearl fishing. You see, two years before, he'd been in the pearl *buying* business, one of the important men in Doolan, until he'd speculated, bought up the whole season's pearl catch, and then Jim Doray, his best friend, had stolen the lot and vanished, leaving Uncle Scully hopelessly in debt. "Oh, that Jim Doray!" he was always telling us. "One o' these bright days I'll meet up with him, the creepin' cuttlefish!"

Perhaps it was mere bravado over the shark that made McGuire obstinate that morning. At any rate he said unexpectedly: "We'll try a dive here, Scully. Drop the hook and I'll look round."

"There's no pearl shell in Blackbirder Channel!" Uncle Scully cried. "Ye know that as well as I do, Dan McGuire. Nobody ever wastes time divin' here!"

"That's why we should maybe," McGuire returned with his easy grin. He winked at me and grinned, with a flash of his glassy eyes. Those eyes were the only unpleasant feature he had, and I used to wonder if it was because he dived so much. But Uncle Scully gave the order for me to stop the motor, and for Umoo, our black kanaka, to let go the anchor. Umoo made up the rest of our crew. He was a wonderful skin or naked diver, but he would never consent to step into any sort of diving dress.

minutes later they began to thicken and whiten, and his water-distorted shape appeared, rising quickly. His head broke surface, a muscular hand gripped the boat's ladder, the sun flashed on his brown shoulders, and he was grinning at us through his glass dive mask. Alongside him was his string bag, so crammed with pearl shell oysters that we could hardly lift it aboard!

That was the beginning of a harvest for the *Williwai*. Every dive McGuire made – and he kept us recharging his air cylinders all day – he brought up a bulging haul

There, in a lonely creek, I spied a small launch.

For comparatively shallow water McGuire used a self-contained frogman outfit. Within a few minutes he was ready for the dive, dressed only in bathing trunks and his essential diving gear – two aluminium compressed-air cylinders strapped to his back, mouthpiece and dive mask. He was laughing as usual as he slipped on the glass mask. It was ten fathoms deep here, and no doubt deeper farther into the channel. He went over the side; I handed him the string bag which he attached to his belt, then he twisted round, slipped into the sea and went boring downwards into the blue-green depths with a steady thrash of his swim fins.

He was right below us, we knew, because his exhaust air bubbles reached the surface in a stream. Fifteen

of the finest gold-lip shell. So much for the widespread belief that Blackbirder Channel was a waste of time for divers!

Umoo went down a few times, with a clip on his nose, and a stone made fast to a line to take him quickly to the bottom; but it was too deep for a skin diver. Next day when we edged farther into the channel he was compelled to give up. Indeed, it was really beyond the safety depth for McGuire's frogman outfit, but he preferred it to the orthodox diving dress.

Two days passed quickly. We worked farther and farther into the channel and we got more pearl shell in that time than we'd done in the previous two months. Uncle Scully was overjoyed, and the atmosphere aboard the *Williwai* was like that at a wedding party, except for Dan McGuire. For he who had been full of jokes and smiles had become thoughtful and quiet, as though he had some worry on his mind.

On the third morning there was a little breeze which ruffled the surface of the inland sea behind the Great Barrier Reef. McGuire made ready for his first dive of the day, and we were glad to see that he had recovered his good spirits. He was actually laughing as he slipped on his dive mask, and I recall watching his powerful figure plunge downwards on its seventy foot-journey to the sea bottom.

When he hadn't reappeared after twenty-five minutes the three of us on deck stood at the gunwale watching for him. At that depth he had only sufficient air for thirty minutes. Uncle Scully was soon looking again and again at his watch. His wrinkled face had gone pale under his tan, his lips were twitching nervily. "Dam' fool," he was saying in a shrill voice. "He's jammed in a clam shell . . . or he's gone too deep in that frogman gear and his chest's caved in. I warned him . . ."

We lay at anchor three hours longer in the blue waters of Blackbirder Channel, but Dan McGuire never appeared. His air had been exhausted long ago. Strong and resourceful though he had been, he had met his match somewhere in the misty fathoms of the channel.

As the crow flies it was only a few miles to Doolan, but it was dusk before the *Williwai* got there because we had to weather a headland called Wreck Point. Uncle Scully reported McGuire's death to the authorities, and that night he consoled himself with a bottle of gin. But by the morning he had ceased to grieve over McGuire and was once again distressed by his own bad luck.

"What a sin for all that lovely shell goin' to waste in Blackbirder Channel," he sighed as we sat together on deck. "It fair makes me heart bleed, Harry. I can see what's ahead o' you and me, lad, we're goin' to end up as a couple o' beachcombers on Doolan waterfront. For where can I get me a diver in the middle o' the season ? What a fool McGuire was to get hisself killed! It's too deep for Umoo, and the black heathen won't step into a diving dress, and me with me nerve gone . . ."

Heaven knows what made me offer. Of course I'd been down in diving dress before, in the frogman outfit too – for in the pearling business folk learn to dive early – but I'd only been in shallow "safe" water, where I could be watched from the boat's deck. But I offered my services, and Uncle Scully astonished me by bursting into tears.

"Oh, no, no, Harry! I couldn't let ye do it. What would your poor mother say ? God bless her soul. Of course it's not really deep. When I was your age I'd been down fifteen fathom! Ye wouldn't hardly have to move a step to get that shell. There's tons of it . . ."

WITHIN the hour we were under way, and that same afternoon we dropped anchor once more in Blackbirder Channel. We got out the old rubber diving dress, with the copper helmet and lead boots. The air hose was coupled up to the deck compressor. Uncle Scully was nearly in tears with gratitude as he and Umoo helped me on with the bulky dress. At last I groped my way down the ladder, with air hissing into my helmet, and sank under the surface on the end of my lifeline. Bubbles from my exhaust valve fluttered upwards. Soon the hull of the *Williwai* became a vague outline on the silvery surface. Looking down I saw the sand and the red and white coral of the channel floor. My boots touched bottom.

I could see the oysters growing amongst the weed and coral rocks. As I swayed through the yielding water a shadow suddenly darkened over me. Glancing up through the top glass of my helmet I saw the livid belly of the White Pointer. Blackbirder Channel must have been the haunt of the solitary monster. Pale as a ghost the mackerel-shaped beast passed within two fathoms of me, a ghoulish glimmer in its icy eye. It swerved past the gurgling stream of air bubbles and vanished into the green walls of the sea.

My heart was beating fast but I forced myself to tear an oyster from its hold and I crammed it into my string bag. Ten minutes passed and I nearly had my bag full when I sensed a movement above me. Then something drifted past my face glass. It was the end of my lifeline – it had been cut through!

At once I gave four tugs on my air hose – the alarm signal. I screwed shut my exhaust valve to gain buoyancy to help as they hauled me up with my air hose. But these precautions were useless, for next instant the lacerated fragment of my air hose fell slowly past my helmet. Now I couldn't get back to the surface at all in this kind of suit, and all I had left of life was the air in my helmet, which I was gasping away with every breath. I w s cut off on the sea floor. Breathing was soon like a knife in my chest. The sea darkened round me as I fell to my knees, suffocating. One despairing look upwards I gave before my senses were blotted out, and I saw a face peering at me through an owlish glass, *the face of Dan McGuire!*

When I opened my eyes I thought it couldn't be in this world. But Uncle Scully was bending over me.

The booby hatch was thrown back.

Tears were running down his cheeks, for he was a man who showed his feelings easily. My helmet was off, but I still lay in the diving dress on the hatch top of the lugger. Opposite me, against the bulwarks, I saw Umoo, dripping wet, chest heaving, blood trickling from nose and mouth. It was he I had to thank for my life. When they had realised that my lines had been severed, the black diver had instantly plunged down with the end of my lifeline at his waist, and an iron shackle in his hands to take him swiftly to the bottom. He had found me there on the sea bed, twelve fathoms deep, where the water pressure drove blood from his mouth and nose; and he'd made fast the lifeline to my belt, tugged a signal on it to Uncle Scully, then struck out for his own life to the surface.

We were under way back to Doolan before I told them my story. Uncle Scully didn't know what to think. I didn't know what to think myself. Those last fevered conscious moments on the sea floor were churned up in my memory. I couldn't, I *couldn't* have see Dan McGuire; but had it been his ghost, as Umoo thought, or had it been imagination?

That evening, as the *Williwai* lay tied up by the sea wall, and Uncle Scully was drinking gin in Fu Chow's saloon, I went for a stroll along the waterfront, and outside the cargo sheds I heard a group of schoonermen discussing how Ken Brin's little motor launch, with a Booster hand pump aboard, had been stolen the prev-

ious night. It was an unheard of thing for anyone to steal a boat in these parts. The significance of this incident struck home to me. Who on earth in Doolan would want to steal a motor launch and a Booster hand pump? Then it occurred to me that a Booster pump could recharge air cylinders on a self-contained diving outfit!

It needed an hour, perhaps an hour and a half, before dark, and by the jungle track, which cuts off Wreck Point, I could reach the shore opposite our diving spot in Blackbirder Channel. I stopped only to take a pair of binoculars from the lugger's cabin, then I set off along the foreshore. At the Wreck Point headland I took to the jungle track, and kept to it until I reached the hillside above some mangrove creeks by the shore of Blackbirder Channel.

The sun was sinking into the Queensland jungles; the sea towards the Barrier Reef was turning crimson. And there, in a lonely creek amongst the green mangroves, I spied a small launch. There was a man aboard it, working on with what appeared to be air cylinders. I saw him clearly through my binoculars. It was Dan McGuire – he was alive!

That night I argued a long time with Uncle Scully, but the fact that I'd actually seen McGuire overruled his objections, so he did what I asked and borrowed some frogman gear for me. At first light we sailed back to Blackbirder Channel, and by mid morning we were once again at anchor over that fatal spot.

It was a brilliant day, the sea like glass. Kingfish and rays were jumping here and there. I knew McGuire would be watching us from the shore, so we hoisted up the ordinary diving dress as though we were drying it out. My idea was to bluff McGuire into thinking that we were not diving at present. For I realised that it was he who had cut my lines the day before, and I knew that if he saw me descend he would enter the sea himself to intercept me.

Uncle Scully didn't want me to do this; but a kind of reckless curiosity had taken absolute charge of me. I dressed in bathing trunks, put on the frogman gear then, carefully, so as not to be in view from the shore, I slipped into the sea on the outward side of the *Williwai*. I swam down into the depths, the water like silk on my limbs, fish trailing me curiously, until I could see the bottom, then I coasted slowly shorewards.

I was so sure that McGuire had discovered something surprising down here, and I wanted to find it too. I came across it within a minute or two. At first it looked like a rock, it was so encrusted with shell, coral and weed. Then I made out a mast, cabins, a rudder, a propeller green with mould. It was the wreck of a motor lugger, or perhaps the remains of an excise cutter, or a fishery patrol boat. Soon I was hovering over its decks, gazing into the black entrances to cabins; then my interest was chilled as my eye fell on a stream of bubbles rising from beyond the forward cabin of the wreck.

I knew at once that McGuire must have come down after all, and I knew also that my own escaping air must betray my presence, if it hadn't done so already. I contemplated making a dash back to the *Williwai;* but if he saw me I wouldn't have a chance. The man was an ace swimmer and diver, and I was the merest amateur in comparison.

WAS he searching the forepart of the wreck, I wondered? If so his air wouldn't last as long as mine, for he had farther to travel to the shore than I had to the lugger. With this thought in mind I ventured down through the booby hatch into the after cabin, where I supposed my exhaust air would not draw attention. Wriggling like an eel I worked my way into the watery gloom of the cabin, risking unguessed horrors in my anxiety to keep clear of McGuire.

I waited there, watching the patch of light above the open hatchway, occasionally peering through a porthole out on to the sea floor where the visibility was amazingly good. I was counting the minutes past, breathing as gently as possible to conserve my air, when I saw a barely recognisable figure swirl above the open booby hatch. There were bursts of exhausted air bubbles. Then the hatch cover crunched home and the light was shut off. McGuire had trapped me!

I fought on with that hatch until my arms ached, my lungs ached, and my heart ached. I knew I was using up my precious air wholesale; but McGuire, with his deadly thoroughness, had secured the hatch against me on the outside. As I wrestled on with it my mind toiled with McGuire's motives. Of course he had found this wreck, perhaps on his very first dive. He had disappeared by swimming ashore, then that night he'd gone to Doolan and stolen the launch with the Booster hand pump. He wanted the pump so that he could dive on his own account to the wreck. For it was this wreck, I was sure, which had induced his murderous state of mind.

At last I sank back into the cabin and desperately examined the portholes, but a dog couldn't have got through any of them. I gazed out again over the misty sea bed. A figure was taking shape in the sea, approaching with slow motion robot steps. I saw the helmet, the lines; it was a diver, and could only have come from the *Williwai*. My exhaust air escaping through the porthole guided him to the wreck. Before long leaden boots thudded overhead. There was a tugging at the booby hatch cover. It was thrown back and the welcome light appeared. As I squirmed upwards I saw Uncle Scully's face behind the glass of the helmet. But my pressure gauge told me my air was nearly done, so I was off like a fish for the *Williwai*.

Uncle Scully also managed to get back to the lugger, but he was a long, long time after me. As he sat there on the hatch top, with his helmet off, he laughed shakily at his experience, and indeed he had every reason to be shaky, for he had come down for me after both Umoo and he had seen what happened to McGuire. After trapping me in the cabin McGuire must have been leaving the wreck, short of air, when the shark attacked him. In an effort to escape he had come to the surface, but it had been his day to die. Ninety-nine times out of a hundred Uncle Scully had said, but it was surely the hundredth time for Dan McGuire when the White Pointer got him that day in Blackbirder Channel.

It did not take Uncle Scully long to explain to me that he had recognised the wreck on the bottom of the channel, just as McGuire must have recognised it as soon as he saw it or, for that matter, as any other diver out of Doolan would have done. For it was Jim Doray's boat! Doray, speeding away from Doolan on a moonless night, must have ripped the bottom out of his motor lugger on a reef and perished with it.

After freeing me down there Uncle Scully had remained long enough to search the forward cabin and to salvage a rusted tin box -- for he'd known better than McGuire where to look for it! And when we opened the box on the *Williwai*'s deck I realised what lay behind Dan McGuire's weird plan for keeping his knowledge of the wreck to himself. That box was full of pearls, the pearls Jim Doray had stolen from my uncle long ago!

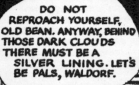

...DRAWER AND CUPBOARD...LOOKED UNDER BEDS....UP CHIMNEYS.

...DUG HOLES...PULLED UP FLOORBOARDS...FELT FOR HIDDEN PANELS...

BUT, UNKNOWN TO WALDORF AND CECIL, GRABBER-GRIBBLE HAS BEEN ABLE TO WITNESS THEIR DISCOVERY THROUGH HIDDEN TELEVISION CAMERAS.

THEY'VE TUMBLED TO MY GUILTY SECRET. I MUST DO SOMETHING... SOMETHING CONCRETE.

CONCRETE!

GRABBER-GRIBBLE, YOU'RE A GENIUS!

LUCKY I HAPPENED TO HAVE A SPARE CONCRETE MIXER KNOCKING ABOUT!

THIS SHOULD CEMENT THEIR FRIENDSHIP.

DOWN BELOW.

GOODNESS! WHAT'S THAT?

IT LOOKS LIKE SECOND-HAND ICE-CREAM, BUT IT TASTES LIKE CEMENT.

YES, DEAR BOY. PERHAPS WE HAD BETTER TAKE OUR DEPARTURE.

IT'S CREEPING TOWARDS US, CECIL!

BUT HOW? THERE'S NO WAY OUT!

CECIL, WE'RE TRAPPED!

OUR ONLY HOPE IS TO TRY AND ARREST ITS PROGRESS WITH THIS CINEMA SCREEN, DEAR CHAP.

ALL TOGETHER NOW— HEAVE!

DO YOU SEE WHAT WAS HIDDEN BEHIND THE SCREEN, WALDORF?

WHAT IS IT, CECIL?

GOLLY! IT'S A BIG ZIP FASTENER.

HOW TO BUILD
Model Planes

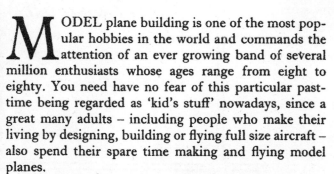

**An Introduction
to this most
popular hobby
by Bill Dean**

MODEL plane building is one of the most popular hobbies in the world and commands the attention of an ever growing band of several million enthusiasts whose ages range from eight to eighty. You need have no fear of this particular pasttime being regarded as 'kid's stuff' nowadays, since a great many adults – including people who make their living by designing, building or flying full size aircraft – also spend their spare time making and flying model planes.

If you have yet to build your first model plane, don't be put off by thinking that a lot of expensive tools and equipment will be needed. Far from it, as even quite advanced models can be made with the aid of some old razor blades, a few pins, pliers and sandpaper. Later on it will help if you extend your collection of tools to include a fretsaw, hand drill, small hammer, modelling knife, files, soldering iron and a small vice – but in the early stages all you need are the few simple items

Only simple tools are needed to build model planes. Balsa is available in block, sheet and strip.

previously mentioned. An old kitchen table, drawing board or even a smooth unwarped plank will provide a fine building surface.

The basic material for building model planes is a remarkably light South American wood called *Balsa*, which is available in many different sizes of block, strip and sheet. Balsa is soft enough to be easily cut with a sharp razor blade of either the single (as shown) or double-edged type. A special quick-drying adhesive, known as *Cement*, is used to join the various parts together and the completed frameworks are covered with lightweight tissue – the latter being tightened and strengthened by applying several coats of *Clear Dope*. Steel piano wire is used for making airscrew shafts, undercarriage legs and similar parts – while thin ply, dowel and other hardwoods are used at certain highly stressed points. Many specialised accessories are produced for the aeromodeller, including airscrews of all shapes and sizes, wheels, fuel tanks, rubber strip, cockpit covers and transfers – to name just a few.

As with most hobbies, success and enjoyment from model plane building depends to a large extent on getting off on the right foot. It's a waste of time and money simply to buy a bundle of materials haphazardly and then start building something that vaguely resembles a full size aircraft, since the layout and proportions for successful models differ considerably from their full size counterparts. In time, practical experience will provide you with sufficient knowledge to enable you to design your own models, but in the first instance you should

MAKE THIS JET-POWERED
HAWKER HUNTER

This Jetex 50 powered flying model of the famous Hawker Hunter takes just a single evening to build. Start by tracing the parts on to sheet balsa and then cut them out with a sharp razor blade – using a ruler as a guide for the straight cuts. The cockpit, R.A.F. markings and control surface outlines may be marked on the wood with coloured ball-point pens *before* the model is assembled. Round off the fuselage corners with sandpaper (except at tailplane position) and cement a 1″ x ¼″ x ⅛″ piece of hardwood to one side (see front and side views). Cement asbestos paper – contained in Jetex 50 outfit – to the other side and screw the motor clip in position.

Round off the edges of the flying surfaces (except wing and fin roots). Sand wing roots to slight angle and cement together – pinning one panel down flat and packing up the other 1¼″ at the tip. When dry, slide wing into slot in fuselage and well cement, after carefully checking for correct alignment. Add small 'X' fairing pieces. Now cement tailplane to fuselage, followed by fin. Push a pin into the fuselage as indicated, attach the *loaded* motor and check that the model balances level. Drawing pins may be pushed into the nose or tail to obtain correct balance.

Glide test the model on a calm day – gently launching from shoulder height and noting if it dives or 'stalls'. Correct a nose dive by removing weight from the nose or adding it to the tail. If the model's nose rises abruptly and then falls (stalling), add more nose weight. A turn in either direction is required, but if the model turns too sharply correct by pushing a drawing pin into the wing tip on the *outside* of the turn. When satisfied with the glide, ignite the charge, *wait several seconds* for thrust to develop, then launch on an even keel. Choose a space clear of trees and buildings as the model is capable of long duration flights of up to a quarter of a mile.

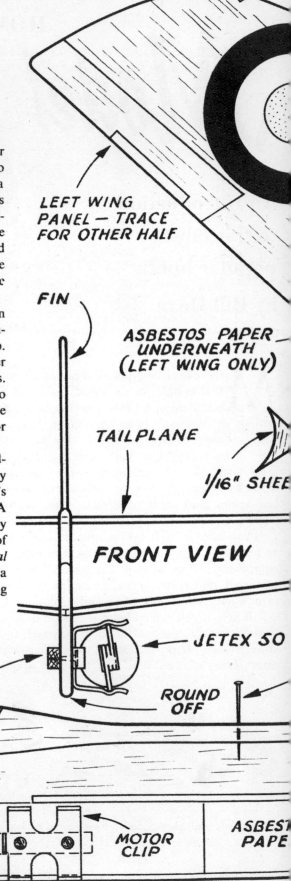

LEFT WING PANEL – TRACE FOR OTHER HALF

FIN

ASBESTOS PAPER UNDERNEATH (LEFT WING ONLY)

TAILPLANE

1/16″ SHEET

FRONT VIEW

JETEX 50

HARDWOOD

ROUND OFF

1/8″ SHEET (MEDIUM HARD) FUSELAGE

HARDWOOD

MOTOR CLIP

ASBESTOS PAPER

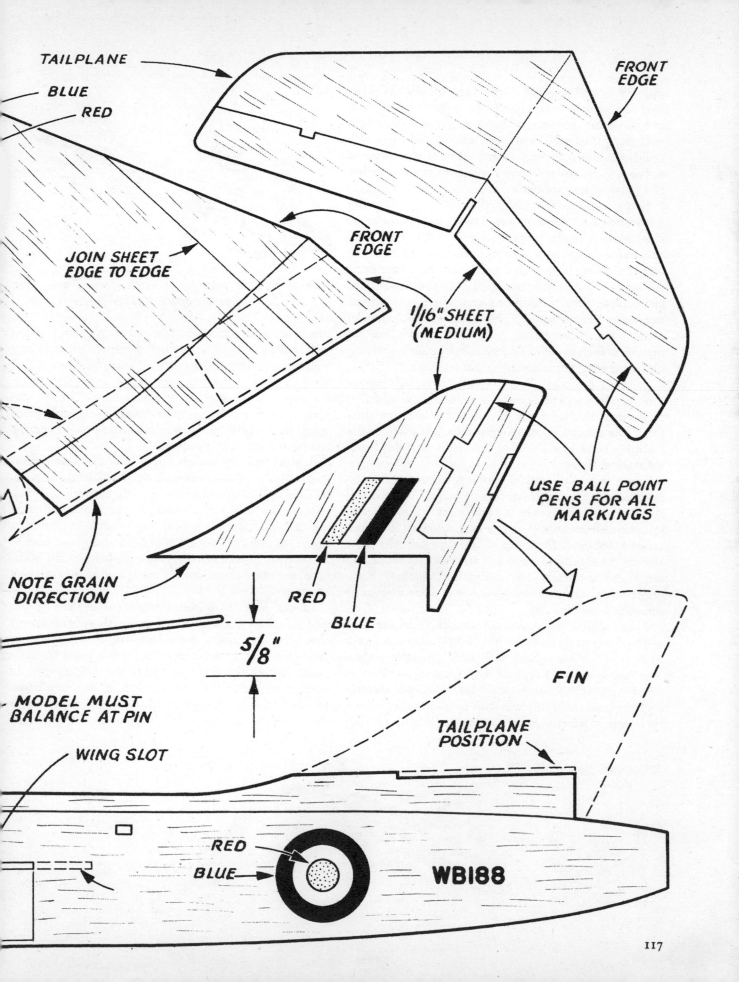

TAILPLANE

BLUE

RED

FRONT EDGE

JOIN SHEET EDGE TO EDGE

FRONT EDGE

1/16" SHEET (MEDIUM)

USE BALL POINT PENS FOR ALL MARKINGS

NOTE GRAIN DIRECTION

RED

BLUE

5/8"

FIN

MODEL MUST BALANCE AT PIN

TAILPLANE POSITION

WING SLOT

RED

BLUE

WB188

start off by building one of the many simple kits available. These may be purchased for as little as 1/6 each and have the advantage that you get just the right amount of materials you need *and no more* – which avoids wasteful spending on such items as 36 in. lengths of balsa sheet, when all you really need is a few inches of a particular thickness.

Kits are available for every conceivable type of model – from beautiful diesel-powered flying scale types to the most advanced radio control designs. Full size plans are always featured – so that components may be built flat on the building board – and sheet parts are either printed on balsa or already stamped out. The majority of kits include detailed building and flying instructions, frequently illustrated with photographs of each stage of construction. Everything you need in the way of materials, such as celluloid for cabin windows, covering tissue, cement, wire, dowel – right on down to the last washer, are provided. Hard to make parts, such as airscrews, nose plugs and cowlings are usually moulded in plastic and ready for use. Some of the new prefabricated kits require no shaping at all – just a few hours assembly work being needed before the model is ready for its first flight.

Many would-be model builders choose a far too complicated kit for their first attempt. An all-sheet glider is best as it takes only a few hours to build, stands up well to hard knocks and is easy to repair if it does become damaged. Most kits of this type have the parts already cut to outline shape and after a little sandpapering these are ready for cementing together. Solid gliders weigh only an ounce or less and are thrown or catapulted into the air.

After building one or two of these simple models, you will be ready to tackle something a little more advanced, such as a tow-line glider with built-up construction. The fuselage of this type of model usually consists of square section balsa strip – the sides being made directly over the plan (held in place with pins) and then joined by means of sheet formers or strip cross pieces. Wing

Turn to previous page for full-size plans of this Jetex powered model of the Hawker Hunter.

construction for this type features strip spars, leading and trailing edges – a cambered upper surface being achieved by fitting sheet ribs. Tailsurfaces are either built up in a similar manner or cut from thin sheet. Built-up frameworks are much lighter than the all-sheet type and although quite fragile in the uncovered state, are surprisingly strong once the tissue covering has been applied and doped.

A small rubber powered model is the next logical step – the construction of such a type following on similar lines to that described above, with the addition of an airscrew assembly and undercarriage. Flying surfaces are usually attached to build-up models with rubber bands, to prevent damage in crashes and allow them to be taken to pieces for carrying purposes. Small built-up glider and rubber kits for models of 20 in. span cost about 4/-.

Larger and more complicated rubber and glider models are available in kit form for those who favour this type, but many modellers will be impatient to tackle a power model next. Until a few years ago, this meant using a petrol engine and all the weighty ignition equipment that went with it, such as coil, condenser and batteries, but nowadays this type of powerplant has been largely superseded by compact self-contained

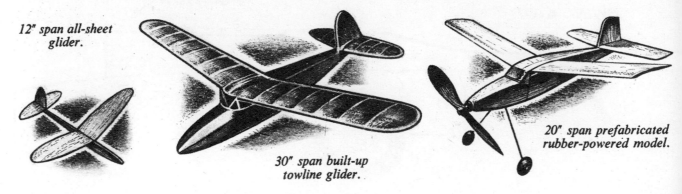

12" span all-sheet glider.

30" span built-up towline glider.

20" span prefabricated rubber-powered model.

diesel, 'glo-plug' or rocket motors. Simplest of these is the rocket type, which is available in several sizes, operates on solid fuel and is ignited by means of a special fuse. Models fitted with these motors are simple to trim and may be of either all-sheet or built-up construction. Full size plans and building instructions for an all-sheet scale model of this type are featured on pages 116 and 117. The cost of the building materials and the Jetex 50 rocket motor for this 11 in. span design works out at a little under 15/-.

Turning to diesel (or 'glo-plug') powered models, we find that these are split into two distinct categories – free flight, which are at the mercy of the wind once launched, and control line, which fly in a circular flight path and are controlled by wires running from the model to a handle held by the operator. The simplest free flight model is not unlike a large rubber powered type in which the nose has been shortened; a diesel substituted for the rubber power and the structure generally toughened up. Motor run is limited by carefully measuring out the fuel or fitting a special timing device.

Diesel powered scale models have become very popular over the last few years – especially of the high-wing cabin types such as the Auster and Piper Cub, which come closest to the most desirable model layout – from a stability viewpoint. For contest flying, realism and appearance are sacrificed in order to produce a highly powered, fast climbing model, capable of putting up a long flight duration on a limited motor run. These models are rather tricky to trim and recommended for only the most experienced modellers. A small free flight kit of 36 in. span may be bought for 11/- and the diesel to fit it, for 49/6.

Control line models are the closest thing to 'real aircraft', since they are made to climb and dive by means of moveable elevators – which are operated by the 'pilot' through UP and DOWN lines attached to a control handle. The control lines must be kept taut at all times, but centrifugal force ensures this – the pilot only having to remember to step back to retain tension in the event of sudden gusts of wind when the model is upwind. Simple trainers are usually made of sheet, but the more advanced stunt type employ lightweight built-up construction. Speed models are mostly made from sheet and block, and are capable of speeds as high as 150 m.p.h. Small control line kits (and engines) cost about the same as free flight kits.

The most recently developed type of control line model is the team racer – which is fashioned on semi-scale lines and has to conform to definite design requirements which cover engine size, wing area and fuel tank

Some typical Free Flight and Control Line power models. From the top these are: 60″ Span Semi-Scale Free Flight; 36″ Span Scale Free Flight; 18″ Span Control Line Speed Model; 30″ Span Control Line Team Racer; 20″ Span Control Line Biplane Sport Model. At bottom right is an Elfin 2.49 Diesel motor.

capacity. These models are raced three or four in a circle – for 160 or 200 laps, depending on the line lengths being used. As each model runs out of fuel and glides in for a landing, the pilot's pit men race to the model, refuel the tank, flick over the airscrew and have the model airborne again – all in a matter of 10-30 seconds. By the time the chequered flag falls for the winner, the atmosphere is tense with excitement – not the least of the fun being in watching the antics of the pilots in the centre of the circle as they try to avoid getting in each others way, without taking their eyes off the models for even a split second. These models fly at speeds of from 60 to 90 m.p.h., so a very high standard of flying skill is essential for all those who take part in T.R. contests.

The most advanced development in aeromodelling is the radio controlled type, which is controlled from the ground by means of a miniature transmitter which sends out impulses that give right or left rudder and in some cases even alter the engine speed to allow 'circuits and bumps' to be made. Already there are several hundred modellers in the country who specialise in this branch of the hobby – which holds exciting promise for the future. Other highly specialised types are multi-engined control line scale models of such aircraft as the Brabazon – and jet powered speed models, fitted with small 'buzz-bomb' type jet units, which fly at speeds as high as 175 m.p.h. Free flight scale designs of jet aircraft are now being propelled by means of diesel driven fans (tucked away out of sight inside the fuselage), to provide a realistic simulation of jet flight.

In addition to the hundreds of model kits available, new designs appear month by month in the aero-modelling periodicals. Some plans are given full size, while others are made available through Plan Service schemes. These magazines also feature articles about new model developments, reports of the many contests which are held every weekend during the flying season (April to September) and news of the activities of the model aircraft clubs scattered throughout the country. The best advice if you are at all interested in building model planes is to first of all join a club – where you will be able to obtain tips on building and flying from more experienced modellers and in many cases, enjoy the use of a well equipped club workshop – all for the price of a moderate subscription fee.

If you write to the Society of Model Aeronautical Engineers, Londonderry House, 19 Park Lane, London W.1, the Honorary Secretary will be only too pleased to let you have the address of your nearest club. The S.M.A.E. is the 'Royal Aero Club' of the model plane world (they even share the same headquarters) and the official body governing all model aviation activities in Great Britain. Joining an affiliated club makes you eligible to enter contests organised by the Society and to qualify for teams which are sent to other countries to represent Britain at International model contests.

The biggest event in the aeromodelling calendar is the 2-day British Nationals at which the pick of the country's modellers meet to do battle for top modelling honours. Gala days and rallies are also held at airfields belonging to such well known aircraft manufacturers as Hawker's and Handley Page. However, in addition to all these big meetings most local clubs turn up for model flying at the local airfield or park, most fine weekends during the year. So why not get started on that first model right away and then go along and join them!

LOUIS . . .

Copyright opera mundi

Spy MESSENGERS

Methods used by spies to deliver their vital information

DESCRIBED BY BERNARD NEWMAN

SUPPOSE you are a spy, working in enemy country in war-time. You secure a piece of valuable information. How are you going to get it back to your headquarters?

In fact, you face one of the greatest problems of the secret agent. When you were at your Spy School your tutor opened one lecture by saying: 'A spy's greatest difficulties lie along his lines of communication.'

This is perfectly true. You may not be able to burgle the War Office safe and steal the 'plans', but it is not difficult to pick up bits and pieces of useful information. But how are you going to get them home?

Radio? Yes, in some circumstances. If you are operating in a friendly country, a confederate may put a set at your disposal. Or if you have been despatched on a special mission, you may carry a portable set.

It has its dangers. The enemy will be testing all wavelengths on his detection apparatus, and should he chance on yours the police or counter-spies will soon be speeding in your direction.

German spies landed in England often carried a very

ingenious portable set packed in two leather cases. In emergency one man could carry it, but it was designed for two. In order to defeat our listening monitors, two spies would cycle into the country, fling an aerial over a tree, tap off their message quickly, and get away before their location could be traced and surrounded.

There are obvious limitations to the possibilities of radio. And how are you going to explain a transmitting set if the police find one in your luggage? Thus it is not surprising to find that older ideas are still current – in your Spy School the tuition will concern the methods of the first World War as thoroughly as those of the second.

Some of these were very ingenious. I remember one man who was never caught. He was an Alsatian – not all Alsatians are dogs! – and had worked for the Germans as a spy messenger. After the war he became a French citizen, and was able to talk. One day, with a French officer, I met him.

"But how did you escape us for four years?" the Frenchman asked.

"I'll show you. Would you like to go out?"

When we returned, he said: "Right. I've got a message concealed on me. Search me."

We were fairly good at searching, and began by ripping the lining out of his clothes. When we started to cut his shoes in two he thought it time to stop us.

His method was quite simple – the simple methods are often the best. He wrote his message on a piece of cigarette paper, crushed it into a tiny ball, plucked out his glass eye, put the paper inside it, and put his eye back again!

If you were a frontier guard, would you have thought of stopping everybody and making them take out their eyes for examination?

Women make very good spy messengers – they are usually poor spies, but are often very clever at thinking out ideas for getting information home.

In the first World War the Germans occupied Belgium but not Holland. One of our headaches was to get information from Belgium into Holland, where our Intelligence officers were always waiting. One Belgian girl never let us down. When all the stock devices had been caught out, she invented one of her own. When she had a message to carry, she would take off her blouse, get a friend to write the message in chemical (or 'invisible') ink on her bare back, and let it dry. There was nothing to be seen, so she put on her blouse and crossed into Holland. When she had contacted our Intelligence officer, she would take off her blouse again, and sit with her back close to the fire. Many chemical inks are affected by heat; this one was, and the message would appear, faintly, on her back. The Intelligence officer

would copy it down, and then the girl went off for a bath. Simple!

I remember a Swiss girl who was very clever with her needle. She was working for the Germans, and part of her job was to make a round of resident agents in France and return to Switzerland with details of the British line of battle – that is, the position of all our divisions. It was impossible to commit a jumble of about 60 numbers to memory, so the girl embroidered them.

When she went into France she was wearing a plain petticoat. By the time she returned it was well embroidered, in a flower pattern. If the first flower were made up of twenty-one stitches, that represented the 21st Division; the next might have thirty stitches, the next seven.

As a variation on this method she would sometimes send presents to little 'nieces' in Switzerland. She would embroider pinafores with childish patterns in cross-stitch – and again her employers had only to count the stitches in order to know which divisions were in line.

Yet some spy messengers used simpler methods very successfully. One German agent led us a pretty dance for nearly two years. She used to get a bar of chocolate, break it in two, scoop out a small hole, and put her message in it. Then she would put the bar together, running a hot knife over the join so as to conceal it. She might never have been caught, but one day she had an accident – she dropped the bar of chocolate and broke it, revealing the piece of paper! A spy messenger cannot afford to make a mistake like that.

Another woman stuffed her message up the wrong

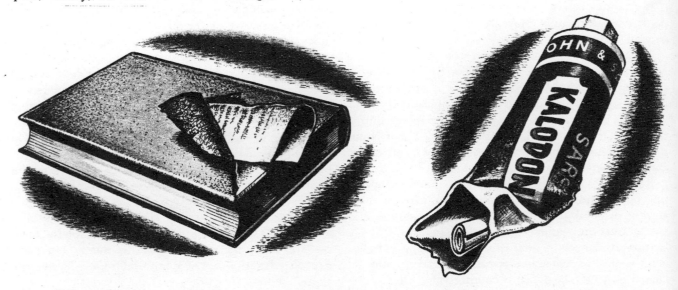

Spies have many ingenious ways of secreting information, two of which are shown above. In one instance the message has been hidden in the binding of a book and in the other, up the wrong end of a tube of tooth-paste.

end of a tube of tooth paste. Hollow keys, ferrules of umbrellas, brims of hats, cakes of soap – all kinds of things have been used for similar purposes.

During the first winter of the last war a British agent in Germany picked up some useful information. How to get it home ? He had a 'brother' in Holland – actually, a skilled Intelligence officer. The man in Germany wrote a family sort of letter, with special and proud mention of his son Wilhelm. In addition to being a good footballer, Wilhelm was also showing the makings of a great artist. In proof, the father enclosed one of the boy's drawing books.

You and I might not have thought very much of Wilhelm's drawings. Nor did the German censor, who passed them without hesitation. But the British Intelligence officer was delighted. The boyish sketches were very varied in their subjects – swans, canaries, throstles, lions, magpies – all crude, but recognisable.

The mention of football gave him the clue to the code which his spy had used. You remember that most football teams have nicknames; Arsenal are the Gunners, Bolton Wanderers the Trotters, Chelsea the Pensioners, and so on. Thus a canary did not suggest the letter C, but N – Norwich City; and a lion stood for M – Millwall. (You might care to make out a code alphabet in full – it is quite easy).

ANOTHER method of spy communication is old enough, but is still in use. You may have met men who could write the Lord's Prayer in the space of a sixpence. They use a very fine pen and a watchmaker's eyeglass, which magnifies everything tremendously. One agent used to draw technical details under a postage stamp. Another man actually wrote 1,800 words and covered them with one stamp !

A most ingenious device was used by a spymaster in a Mediterranean town. He had to give directions to his agents, but did not wish to risk writing or being seen with them. So he invented a very simple method.

The streets of the town were very narrow, to keep out the sun, and the local method of drying clothes was to hang them on a pole across the street. So the spymaster's wife would hang out the washing; then pull it in to re-arrange it or to put new pieces out to dry – and the spies watching from a distance had their orders.

The man used a very simple code – he had worked out an alphabet of clothing. It began something like this –

Apron
Blouse
Collar
Duster

Again, you might like to complete it yourself. The spymaster's wife simply arranged the articles of clothing so as to spell out the message. (Naturally, I have outlined the code in English – in the language used the order was quite different).

Lord Baden Powell, the founder of the Boy Scouts, was a spy when he was a young officer. He was also a clever artist. When he had ferreted out details of a foreign fortress, he would sketch details of its defences. Naturally, he did not do this openly. He would pretend to be a butterfly hunter, and would draw a beautifully-marked butterfly in his sketch book. The darker parts of its markings, very adeptly camouflaged, would represent the sites of the fortifications.

The spy messenger is always in danger. As the woman with the bar of chocolate found to her cost, an

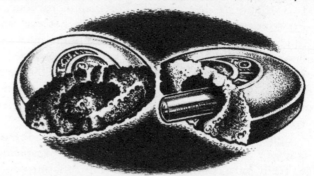

Vital information has been successfully carried in the centre of a cake of soap.

ingenious device is not enough. A good spy thinks out a method of destroying his message if he is likely to be captured. Some have swallowed the pieces of paper they carried. One man used to carry his message in the bowl of his pipe, with tobacco on top of it. Thus, in an emergency, he could smoke it !

He derived this idea from one of Baden Powell's methods. Once in a European country he was held up by a village policeman.

"You'll have to stay here while I send for my inspector," said the man, quite unaccustomed to dealing with suspected spies.

"All right," Baden Powell replied. "I hope he won't be long – I want to catch a train. Do you mind if I smoke while I'm waiting ?"

The policeman agreed. Baden Powell rolled a cigarette in his little pocket machine, and smoked it. Then another. After that he didn't care if a dozen inspectors came. He *had* been spying, but had made his notes on pieces of cigarette paper – which he had now smoked under the very eyes of the policeman who had arrested him!

A mere list of the devices of spy messengers would make fascinating reading. A man goes into a restaurant, hangs up his hat, and sits down to a meal. Another man enters, hangs up a similar hat – and goes out later wearing that brought by the first man. The spy message, of course, is inside the lining.

A man cut open the battery of a torch used in the black-out, and revealed a tightly-compressed document. *This is how a Polish spy brought the first news of the German flying bombs to England.*

Another agent exchanged foreign stamps with a friend abroad. If his letter was post-marked Portsmouth, and he enclosed three Martinique stamps, two Peruvian, four Chilean and six Columbian, that would indicate that on the date the letter was posted there were three battleships, two heavy cruisers, four light cruisers and six destroyers in Portsmouth harbour.

A woman spy got a speck of dust in her eye, and winked to her confederate – in Morse! Some spies still use an old device. Take a new pack of cards, arranged in order of suits. Pencil a message on the edge of the pack; then mix the cards up. Naturally, the message cannot be seen – but when the cards are replaced in their original order, it will be there.

A girl has cut her finger, and has applied an adhesive bandage. Should frontier guards have any suspicion, she really *has* a cut finger – she did it herself, purposely. They might not notice that, for security, she has used *two* sticky bandages; thus they might not guess that a small piece of paper was lodged between them.

I know many spies who have always favoured an ordinary-looking letter as their mode of communication. Suppose a small boy wrote to an uncle in Spain: 'Dear Uncle George, I am getting on very well at school, and my new teacher is nicer than the last. I went to see Aunt Bessie at Plymouth last Saturday. She has three rabbits and seven hens. Do they have choco-

One agent used to draw technical information and write messages under postage stamps.

late in Spain? There isn't much here. With love from Roland.'

Certainly that seems ordinary enough. But if Uncle George were a trained spy he might deduce that on the particular Saturday there were three cruisers and seven destroyers in Plymouth Harbour.

For those who are interested in this side of a spy's work, I recommend a study of the story *Calloway's Code*, by the famous American writer O. Henry. (You will find it in his book called *Whirligigs*). It is studied at spy schools in a dozen countries.

Calloway, in the story, was a newspaper reporter in the Russian-Japanese war of 1904-5. The severe Japanese censorship spoiled all his despatches. But one day he found that a big battle was pending. How could he get the news past the censor?

A day or two later his editor was startled to receive from him a cable so nonsensical that the Japs had passed it without query – obviously it could have no reference to military operations. "Foregone preconcerted rash witching goes muffled rumour mine dark silent unfortunate richmond existing great hotly brute select mooted parlous beggars ye angels incontrovertible."

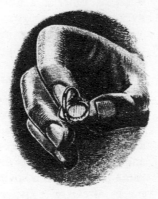

In this case the message has been effectively concealed in the cavity of a jewelled ring.

The editor could make nothing of this jumble of rubbish. Can you? It was left to a very junior reporter to break through Calloway's Code. You will have noticed that many popular newspapers are fond of stock phrases – 'journalese', it is often called. So Calloway had written his message using only one word of a stock phrase. Thus 'foregone' meant conclusion, and 'witching' stood for the hour of midnight; 'dark' was the other half of horse, and 'unfortunate' referred to pedestrians.

The decoded message ran: 'Conclusion arrangement act midnight without saying report hath it host horse majority pedestrians in the field conditions White Way contested force few question times description correspondent unaware facts.'

From this cryptic message an astute editor was able to deduce that the Japanese were advancing to the attack at midnight with a large body of cavalry and an overwhelming force of infantry. Their path was contested only by a small force. *The Times* correspondent's description could be questioned, as he was unaware of the facts. On this foundation expert journalists wrote a thrilling account of the operations and scored a sensational scoop.

Obviously the innocuous letter method depends upon a clever confederate at the home end of the organisation – someone on the same wavelength of thought as the spy, so to speak.

Secret inks – codes – ciphers – all these have their place in the training of the spy messenger. They also have their dangers, for they provide vital evidence if the messenger is caught, or even suspected. The spy is always searching for new ideas – for a method which has once been revealed should be promptly discarded. In one of my early books I had a character, a typist in a military office, use a clean black carbon when typing secret documents. The papers themselves were numbered – but no one thought of looking at the carbon. A German girl read the book, and thought the method so good that she began to use it. Unfortunately for her, the German counter-spies had also read the book, and the girl was executed because she had broken one of the oldest rules of the spy's craft.

In our youth we all want to be spies. Here is an opportunity to test our skill. You are a spy in enemy country, in war-time. You have acquired some vital information about the enemy's stock-pile of atom bombs – much too long to commit to memory, or to risk transmission by radio. How will you get your information home? Can you think of a really novel method by which your spy messenger can carry it? Or can you put it into a chatty letter which will readily pass the censor? Especially, can you invent a device which has never been used?

GRANDPA... BY PROBYN

REX MILLIGAN
marks his man

A COMPLETE STORY BY ANTHONY BUCKERIDGE, ILLUSTRATED BY MAZURE

WE can always be sure of an exciting game when we play St Mark's Boys' Club at rugger. They're heavier in the scrum than our Grammar School pack, and the game usually develops into a pretty hectic sort of hurly-burly before it's over. But this year's fixture turned out to be the most frantic mix-up on record – and, what's more, the trouble had nothing to do with the laws of the game.

It was an 'away' match for us, as we were playing on the recreation ground where St. Mark's are allowed one of the pitches. Plenty of other clubs use the rec. on Saturdays, of course, and everybody changes in one large pavilion, split up into separate rooms. We shared a changing-room with our opponents, and while we were unpacking our kit I made a point of asking Nobby Clarke, the St Mark's captain, about the 'security' arrangements.

"Will it be safe to leave our 'valuables' in here ?" I inquired. "Not that I've got any priceless jewels on me; but I *have* got rather a decent wrist-watch."

"Don't worry," he assured me. "The groundsman will lock this room up as soon as we've gone out on to the pitch. He's pretty hot about that sort of thing: just as well, too, when you look at some of the queer types you find floating around public recreation grounds."

One or two of our chaps had been vaguely wondering where to leave their watches, fountain pens and what-have-you, and they looked a lot happier when they heard that no one could get in the changing-room without the groundsman knowing all about it.

As soon as I'd changed, I went out on to the pitch with Jigger Johnson and we spent a few minutes booting a ball about while we waited for the game to start. Then Nobby Clarke came ambling up, looking about as chirpy as a centipede with chilblains.

"I'm awfully sorry, Milligan," he began, "but I've been checking up on my team, and it looks as though we'll have to play one man short. Old Parslow hasn't turned up, and it's too late to rope in anyone in his place."

Well, that was a mouldy bit of luck for all of us; after all, it takes the shine off the game if one side has to play at a disadvantage.

Jigger scratched his nose thoughtfully and took a squint round the rec. "Why not ask that character over there if he plays rugger," he suggested. "He might be glad of a game."

We followed the direction of Jig's pointing finger and saw a bulky lad of about nineteen ambling aimlessly about the touchline. He was an untidy-looking specimen with a greasy forelock fringing his eyes like a lampshade; his bulk was chiefly fat where it should have been muscle, and he'd got most of it in the wrong place, anyway. Still, he sported a beefy pair of shoulders under his tight, spivish jacket, so there was just a chance he might be able to shove his weight in the scrum.

"He doesn't look my idea of a rugger player," said Nobby doubtfully; "but you can't be too choosey when you're a man short." And he led the way over to the touchline and said: "I say, would you like a game of rugger ?"

The bulky bod smarmed back his forelock and squinted at us suspiciously. Close to, you could see he was pudgy and pimply and even less like an athlete than we'd thought.

"We could fix you up with some kit – that is, if you'd like to play," Nobby explained.

For a few seconds Bulky stood and brooded over the suggestion. Then, in a croaky, catarrhal sort of voice he said: "Don't mind if I do! Done quite a lot of rugger, have. Played for good clubs an' all!"

We took him along to the pavilion and borrowed some spare tackle from the groundsman. The clothes were a bit on the skimpy side, and when he'd squeezed into them, Bulky looked about as natty as a toad in tights. Still, that wasn't going to worry us, provided his rugger was up to scratch.

But it wasn't! As soon as the game started it became pretty clear that the Bulky Type wasn't all that he'd cracked himself up to be. He floundered about like a seal on an ice-rink and was no more use to Nobby's forward line than a left-footed sparrow. What's more, he took mighty good care to keep out of harm's way whenever there was a spot of low tackling on the programme.

"I don't think he's ever played the game before," Jigger muttered to me during a line-out. "Talk about a passenger!"

"Never mind! It's jolly decent of him to turn out, specially to make up the side. You might almost call it his good turn for the day."

I DIDN'T know then how wide of the target my remark was! But the first inkling came a few minutes later when some misguided player thrust the ball into Bulky's hands in such a way that even *he* couldn't fumble the pass. Now, I was his nearest opponent, so naturally I bore down on him all set for a tackle. But even before I'd touched him, he'd hurled the ball up in the air and dropped down on the grass moaning like a fog-horn and yelling blue murder.

"*Ow-aw-ow!*" he wailed. "My ankle – broken it! That's what you've done."

I was so surprised that I stopped in mid-tackle: and as the ball had gone into touch, the ref stopped the game to see what all the hoo-hah was in aid of.

Bulky lay on the ground, clutching his left ankle and writhing in agony – at least, that's what *we* thought!

"What happened, Milligan?" asked the ref.

"I don't know. He collapsed before I had a chance to tackle him," I explained.

"Sprained my ankle – that's what you've done!" moaned Bulky; which was a pretty unfair accusation, all things considered. Then he struggled to an upright position and hopped about on one leg. "I can feel it swelling up. Help me back to the pavilion, someone. Shan't be able to get this boot off if I leave it much longer."

Nobby and I took an arm each and supported the hopping casualty off the field and into the pavilion. After that we rootled out the groundsman and got him to come along with the changing-room key.

"I shall be okay now," said the Bulky Type. "You go

Bulky squinted at us suspiciously.

and get on with the game," He followed the groundsman along the corridor, dragging his left leg painfully behind him.

"Funny – him getting hurt like that!" Nobby remarked as we clattered down the pavilion steps.

I grinned. "He's no more hurt than that goal-post! I reckon the game's turned out to be a lot tougher than he bargained for, so he's making a graceful exit on the strength of a faked injury."

That was my theory, anyway: but like so many theories it overlooked the plainest fact of all.

Well, the match got going again as soon as Nobby and I were back on the field; and in a few minutes the game had grown so lively that we'd forgotten all about our injured substitute. We were in good form that day and belted into the attack like blinko. St Mark's fought back just as strongly, and managed to stop us getting through even though they were playing a man short.

Then, a few minutes before the half-time whistle was due, Jigger whisked the ball clean off the toes of a St Mark's forward and sent a sizzling pass out to me at right-wing three-quarter. I was travelling at full tilt when I caught the ball, and as there was no one directly in front of me it looked as though I was all set for a try. Old Nobby Clarke was pounding across to intercept, of course, but I reckoned I could just beat him to it if I hared flat-out down the touch-line. It was going to be a near thing either way and unless I could . . . And then something happened that wasn't on the programme as advertised.

Out of the corner of my eye I caught a glimpse of a bulky figure a few yards outside the touch-line. He was limping towards the main gate of the rec. and there was something about that limp that struck me as being odd. So I glanced at him again, and this time I noticed an-

came hurtling at me like a jet-fighter bursting through the supersonic barrier. He flung himself in a low flying tackle which took me just above the knees.

Down I went with Nobby on top, and it was some seconds before I could roll clear of him and struggle to my feet. By this time, our bulky friend had made good use of his start, and I knew that if I didn't get cracking pretty smartly it would be good-bye to my watch for ever.

"Hey, Milligan, where are you waltzing off to?"

"Hey, Milligan, where are you waltzing off to?" shouted Nobby as I raced away.

other thing – *the chap was wearing my watch on his wrist!*

Maybe I ought to have seen through his little dodge earlier on: but I'd been so sure that he'd put on his 'injury' act merely because he'd got the wind up, that I never twigged the real reason why he wanted to get back into the changing-room.

It gave me a nasty jolt, I don't mind telling you; and for a split second I forgot about the match and Nobby Clarke and the try I was all set for. And without thinking, I swerved away in pursuit of the Bulky bod. He saw me coming after him and took to his heels – and with no trace of a limp now, either!

But if I'd forgotten about Nobby, he certainly hadn't forgotten about me. As I veered over the touch-line, he

shouted Nobby, as I raced away hot-foot on Bulky's trail.

"Come back – the game's not over yet! What on earth are you playing at?" I heard the ref call from some distance behind me.

Both teams must have thought I'd gone stark, raving cuckoo: but I couldn't waste time making speeches with Bulky Type making himself scarcer every second. So I just yelled: "Follow me, everybody – if you don't want to lose your belongings!"

Most of the chaps hadn't a clue about what was going on; but Jigger and one or two others caught the drift of what I was trying to explain, and came thundering along behind me.

But were we too late? You see, Bulky was legging it

for the exit at a sprightly 15 m.p.h. and once he'd got into the High Street we wouldn't have a hope of picking him up amongst the crowd. Fortunately, though, he wasn't really built for speed, and as I gradually narrowed the distance between us I could hear him wheezing like an asthmatic corncrake.

He reached the gate; then glanced back and saw me only a few yards behind. It put the wind up him so much that he pelted through and straight across the High Street, while bus drivers stood on their brakes and we sent them to various action stations where they could keep tabs on all people leaving the store. Mind you, we got a few stares from shoppers and I don't wonder. After all, you don't see twenty-nine mud-streaked characters in gaudy rugger vests throwing a cordon round a multiple store, every day of the week!

Nobby Clarke went in through the main entrance, while Jigger and I stationed ourselves at the rear. As we took up our positions, Boko Phipps one of the Gram-

Before goggle-eyed passers by, a dozen or so mud-caked characters hurled themselves on him.

cars bounced on their springs in frantic efforts to avoid him.

How he got across without being killed, I don't know! But he did: and by the time I'd waited for the traffic to move out of the way, Bulky had gone to earth somewhere on the opposite side of the road.

"Where is he?" panted Jigger and Nobby, as they charged up behind me.

I pointed to a large multiple stores, the entrance crowded with shoppers.

"I *think* he's bolted in there," I said. "There's another entrance at the back and one in that side street, so we'll have to put a guard on all doors before we go in and look for him."

The rest of the chaps had arrived by now, so

mar three-quarters, came running up, his eyes bulging with indignation.

"I've been into the pav," he panted. "That rotten fraud's been through all our pockets; he must have collared at least six watches. And what's more he had the nerve to take the key back to the groundsman when he'd finished, and thank him very much!"

We waited a few minutes by the rear entrance: and then, sure enough, the glass door swung open and the one-and-only Bulky Type, in person, came marching out. I reckon he'd guessed we'd be waiting for him because he didn't seem all that surprised to see us.

"Come on – hand over those watches," I said.

He looked pained! "Watches!" he echoed. "I haven't touched any watches. You can search me if you like."

We ran our hands over him and prodded his ribs; but there wasn't a whisker of a wrist-watch about him anywhere.

"Satisfied?" he jeered. "Or would you like to listen in case I start ticking?"

I just didn't know what to do next. Bulky had fooled us once already and I wasn't going to let him get away with it a second time. But if we couldn't find those watches, we wouldn't have a leg to stand on when it came to proving anything.

"Keep him here a minute," I told Jigger. "I'll go and see if Nobby's got any ideas on the subject."

THE store was crowded to bursting with shoppers when I pushed my way inside. It was a big place where you could buy anything from carpet-sweepers to corn-plasters, and it took me some time to find Nobby. But at last I spotted him picking his way round perambulators and over dog leads in the jewellery department.

"He's not in here," Nobby greeted me.

"I know. We've got him outside," I explained. "It seems he cleaned up everybody's watches while he was at it."

"You've got them back then!" Nobby sounded relieved.

"No, we haven't. He knew we were after him, so he dumped them somewhere before we could search him."

Nobby looked round the vast, crowded building in despair. "It'd take us a month to search this place," he said. "He might have dropped them in a litter basket or slipped them in somebody's shopping bag or – well, there's a thousand places they might be!"

He was about right, too. We just didn't know where to start looking. And we couldn't detain our bulky friend much longer without producing some evidence against him, so it looked as though we were up a gum-tree, unless . . .

"Golly! Why, of course!" I burst out suddenly, as the obvious answer flashed into what I'm pleased to call my brain. Because it had struck me that the best place to hide things was to put them right under people's noses. And I was ready to bet my boots that Bulky had put those watches in the one place where we wouldn't bother to give them a second glance.

I spun round to the jewellery counter behind me. Amongst the ornaments and ear-rings and brooches was a large tray of wrist-watches: and there, *slap-bang-plonk* in the middle was my own watch!

"Wacko!" I crowed; and picked it off the tray.

Then Nobby spotted his watch in the row above; and in a matter of seconds we'd picked out half-a-dozen that we knew belonged to various members of the teams.

We were so pleased with our detective work that we never stopped to think what our action must have looked like to other people. The jewellery assistant was busy at the far end of the counter, so we wrapped our stolen property in my handkerchief and then made tracks for the door. A tall, thin character in a blue suit followed just behind, but we were far too excited to pay any attention to *him!*

Jigger and Boko were still guarding Bulky a few yards down the street, but we hadn't taken two steps towards them when the blue-suited customer tapped me on the shoulder.

"Excuse me, but I don't think you've paid for those watches," he said curtly.

It was then I realised that Blue Suit wasn't a customer at all. He was the store detective!

"I must ask you to come with me to the manager's office," he went on. "I shall have to communicate with the police about this."

WELL, I ask you! It was mouldy enough losing our belongings in the first place: but being arrested for stealing them, just after we'd done some nifty detective work to get them back – well, that was the last straw!

"You don't understand," I protested. "These watches are ours. Someone stole them and dumped them on your counter."

Yes, I know it sounded a bit thin. The detective raised a disbelieving eyebrow. "I've heard stories like that before," he said grimly.

So I handed the watches over to him and, of course, when he'd examined them he saw that they weren't the store's property after all.

"Here's the chap who's caused all the trouble," I said, and indicated the culprit standing between his two escorts.

Now, our little hoo-hah with the detective had taken place just outside the shop doorway, where Bulky had been unable to see just what was going on. He'd no idea that we'd found our watches, and he was still smirking at his own cleverness when we marched up to him.

"You've been barking up the wrong tree, chum," he greeted me. "I told you I never touched . . ." He stopped abruptly as I unfolded my handkerchief and displayed the loot inside.

That shook him, all right! We'd got a case against him now, and he knew it. For a moment he stood staring guiltily, and then with a sudden movement he wrenched himself free from Jigger and Boko and pelted down the side street as fast as his flat feet would carry him.

He didn't get far! As he reached the corner a dozen or so mud-caked characters in striped vests hurled themselves on him in an untidy rugger scrum. Others came running from the front entrance, and before the goggle-eyed passers-by knew what was happening, a full-scale rugger match was raging all over the pavement and overflowing into the road.

The only thing missing was the ball. But somewhere at the bottom of the scrum was Bulky; and so long as he was there the absence of a ball didn't seem to matter very much!

It took several minutes to straighten out the schemozzle, but at last Bulky was helped to his feet and marched off to the store manager's office.

"They'll think I'm crazy at the police station," said Blue Suit. "They're used to me ringing them up to say I've found someone pinching the stock. But this is the first time I've ever had to fetch them because someone's been *adding* to it!"

It was too late to finish the game by the time we got back to the ground, so we arranged a replay and then went into the pavilion to change.

"What made you twig that our tame substitute was up to a spot of no-good?" asked Jigger, as he struggled into his shirt. "After all, I saw him hoofing away from the pav, but I didn't suspect anything."

"It was his phoney limp," I answered. "When we helped him off the field it was his left ankle that was causing so much trouble. But when he came out again, the pain had mysteriously shifted to his *right* foot. I shouldn't have given him a second glance, if it hadn't been for that."

We're playing St Mark's again next Saturday; but this time I'm going to leave my watch at home!

PICTURE QUIZ

1. Is this plane a Hunter, Javelin or Swift? 2. Can you decide whether this nest is that of a Blackbird, Thrush or Crow? 3. Dismal Desmond's next. Is he a Great Dane, Mastiff or Bloodhound? 4. See if you can land this fish – it's either a Bream, Perch or Roach. 5. This member of the cat family is a Jaguar, Leopard or Cheetah. 6. Here's one for train spotters. The class of this locomotive is Merchant Navy, Schools or King?

Motor Racing and Sports Cars

A REVIEW OF THE PRESENT ERA OF CHANGE

Written by Dudley Noble with colour plates by George Pye

THE present time is a period of changing over from one type of racing car to another, which explains why there has been rather less excitement during the past years in the big international races for Grands Prix. Every free country holds one of these annually, with the exception for the moment of the United States and a few smaller nations. The running of such races is governed by a code which is internationally agreed, and from time to time the regulations dealing with the specification of an acceptable car are changed in order that progress in design shall be made – for, after all, it is acknowledged that racing helps to improve the breed of the ordinary everyday touring car.

The code resolves itself into a formula, and since the war ended this has been graded into three classes. The most important from the international Grand Prix aspect has been Formula I, which laid it down that an engine must be of no greater capacity than 1,500 cubic centimetres if supercharged or three times that capacity if unsupercharged. The capacity of an engine is, of course, its total cylinder volume; that is to say, the amount of mixture, or gas, which can be inhaled by all the pistons – the number of them does not matter. As 1,500 c.c. is a litre and a half, and as a litre is $1\frac{3}{4}$ pints, the volume of a Formula I supercharged engine is $2\frac{5}{8}$ pints and of an unsupercharged one as nearly as possible one gallon. These quantities do not, of course, refer to liquid petrol, but to the gaseous mixture on which an engine runs, consisting of about 14 parts of air to one of petrol vapour.

This formula served its purpose very well, and many successful cars, also the B.R.M., were built to suit it. But, as engine efficiency increased, it became apparent that the cars were becoming too fast for the tracks that were available in almost every country, including the road circuits which are employed for motor racing on the Continent. Road racing has always been forbidden in Great Britain, although the local governments in the Isle of Man, Jersey and Ulster have passed laws enabling racing within their territory at certain times, mainly with an eye on the visitors it brings.

Now we are in the last year in which cars built to Formula I are eligible for participation in international Grand Prix races. The formula has been as good as dead for some little time, because the clubs organising the races in various countries had already switched over to Formula 2, which catered for cars with engines up to 2 litres unsupercharged. This is merely a temporary arrangement, however, pending the introduction at the beginning of 1954 of the new Formula I, which will be for supercharged cars up to only 750 c.c. – half that of the old Formula I – and for unsupercharged cars up to $2\frac{1}{2}$ litres capacity. In passing, it may be remarked that 750 c.c. was about the size of the old Austin Seven engine, the pre-war type. The present Austin Seven's engine is of 803 c.c.

Thus, in most of the recent Grand Prix races, the Formula 2 cars which competed have not been really representative of what may be termed the very latest and best in racing car design. These will no doubt come into the open in 1954, when some really fierce competition may be expected, with Germany challenging Italy once again. In the immediate pre-war days, the German Mercédès-Benz cars, which had strong government backing under the Hitler regime, proved themselves supreme. Had it been possible since to discover the whereabouts of those very cars, they would

Major Goldie Gardner's "Special" M.G., known as the "Magic Midget", holder of many world records.

This Alta has a 4 cylinder engine with overhead camshafts and is a British Formula 2 contender.

The Alfa-Romeo type 158, with straight 8 cyl. engine, was one of the most successful Grand Prix cars.

Now outdated, the Maserati 4CLT with 4 cyl. 1½ litre, 4 valves per cylinder engine, scored many wins.

Built in 1936 as Britain's representative racing car, the E.R.A. has been placed in numerous international races.

This is the 1½ litre Ferrari with single stage supercharger, producing 380 b.h.p. at 7,500 r.p.m.

Mercédès-Benz is a name to conjure with and this is the world-beating 3-litre, 12-cyl. pre-war G.P. racer.

Britain has produced no more successful sports car than the Jaguar XK.120, which averaged 100 m.p.h. for a week.

probably have been good enough to set the pace in post-war racing, but the fact is that they vanished without trace at some period during the hostilities.

Thus the field has been left open to the representatives of Italy, and very worthy ones at that. Alfa-Romeo and Ferrari have been names to conjure with in post-war Grand Prix racing, although the cars themselves were not really brand new post-war designs but largely based on models produced up to 1939. On the other hand, Britain never had a real racing car of thoroughly modern design; the only representative was the E.R.A., a machine which dated from 1936 and was originally based on the Riley. Good though it has been, no privately sponsored job could hope to keep abreast of the times when it came to competing with cars that had national backing with virtually unlimited resources. The best it could do was to get placed now and again in the big races.

To provide Britain with a racing car on somewhat similar lines to the foreigners was the aim and object of Raymond Mays when he put forward his B.R.M. project and got the motor manufacturers to take it up. It was the nearest thing to national sponsorship which could be hoped for in this country. But the whole design had to be evolved from the word go and all the thousands of parts built in a hundred different factories up and down the land. It was neither a quick nor a simple process, and, when it came to testing the first experimental models, there was not a track, not a suitable stretch of road, in Britain where its national racing car could be put through tests to determine the weak spots. Airfield circuits there may be in plenty, but they are not suitable for giving a modern Grand Prix racing car the full bore trials that mean all the difference between winning and merely being placed. We must remember that France, Germany and Italy all have the facilities in this direction that we – the leading motor manufacturing country in Europe – lack.

When it comes to record-breaking, Britain is in a happier position in the international sphere. Lieut-Colonel Goldie Gardner (the "Goldie", let it be mentioned, is really his name, not a nickname, as many people seem to think) took his M.G. "Magic Midget" to Utah during 1952 and put up some speeds which simply are magical for an ordinary production engine, merely fitted with a supercharger. Just on 190 m.p.h. for five miles with the equivalent of a 10 h.p. car is stupendous – no wonder in America the little M.G. has fans galore, and dozens of M.G. Car Clubs holding sports events from coast to coast.

Then there is the Jaguar, whose feats have brought dollars by the million across the Atlantic. It won the famous 24 hour race at Le Mans (France) in 1951, the first time a British car had pulled it off since the old Bentley days.

Of course, the "Jag" isn't a racing car, built to suit an international formula, but a regular production model of sporting type. Its engine is a six cylinder, of $3\frac{1}{2}$ litres capacity, and the cars that do so many amazing things are of the sort that can be bought by the public, whereas a racer is a special job that may have cost hundreds of thousands of pounds to make. At the time of writing perhaps the best of the Jaguar's feats was its 100 m.p.h. for seven days and nights at Montlhéry, the French motor race track near Paris; this took place in August 1952.

Other names which have been prominent on the circuits of Britain and the Continent are Aston Martin, which has won the Gran Turismo category of the renowned Mille Miglia (a thousand miles road race round Italy) two years in succession, Frazer Nash, which made the first ever British victory in the Targa Florio, another stiff Italian race, and the Healey, which did well in the 1952 Le Mans 24 hours race, being the first British car to finish.

The name Bristol, too, has become familiar to racing enthusiasts by virtue of the 2-litre engine being fitted into the chassis of Cooper cars, which normally have air-cooled engines and come into Formula 3 (for engines of capacity not exceeding 500 c.c. – in other words, the little chaps. Motor cycle engines are largely used for these). By fitting the Bristol engine, the Cooper was able to compete with Formula 2 cars like Alta and H.W.M.

Turning to Formula 3, this is a somewhat recent development, because it is only within the last few years that the urge to produce a car which the average none-too-wealthy enthusiast could buy or build, and race, found expression in what may be called the doodle-bug type of car. The craze can be said to have started when father and son Cooper, garage proprietors of Surbiton, built a car which cost very little yet made rings round the bigger jobs. Up-and-coming young men like Stirling Moss drove these little bombshells to victory against stiff opposition and soon there were enough of them to justify races among themselves, so Formula 3 was brought into being. In consequence it looks like being the most popular class pending the coming of the international contenders for honours in the new Formula 1.

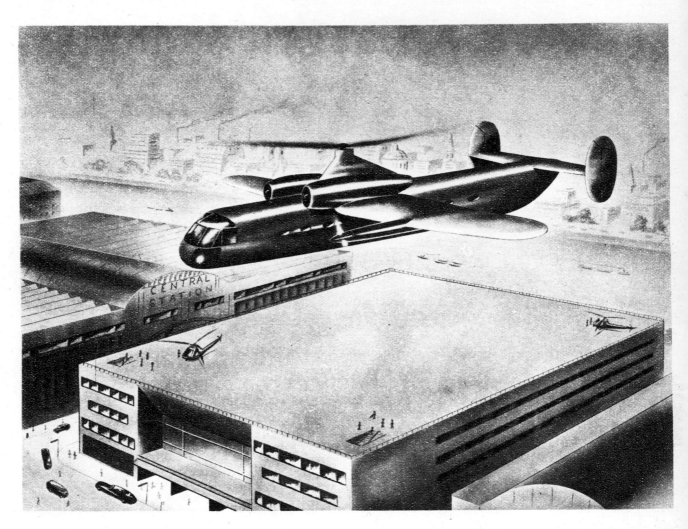

The Air Bus is Coming

Helicopters, Autogiros, Gyrodynes and Rotodynes disentangled by

JOHN W. R. TAYLOR, illustrated by BARRY JONES

COME with me on a quick visit to London Air-port – not as it is today, but as it should be in a few years time (certainly within ten years). It is only an imaginary trip, so we may as well go through the doors marked "Strictly Private", and see everything from the best possible viewpoint – the fine new control tower, standing head and shoulders above the passenger buildings in the middle of the airport and linked with the outside world by underground tunnels under the runways.

Looking past the air traffic controllers, seated by their radio and radar sets, we can see on the tarmac the big gleaming jet-liners that have shrunk the world until even Australia is only 24 hours flying time from London.

We can feel proud that so many of them are British for beneath the colourful airline markings of a dozen countries are the super-Comets and Britannias, big new sweptwing Vickers air liners and the first of the revolutionary "paper dart" Avro Delta-liners.

Now look over to the left where the airline motor coaches used to park, ready to carry thousands of passengers a day on the half-hour journey between the airport and London. They are no longer there. Instead, a fleet of giant 40-seat, jet-propelled helicopters is busy shuttling to and fro over the same route, whisking passengers to London in a mere five minutes, 1,000 ft. above traffic jammed on the Great West Road.

Notice too that there are few small air liners in sight. They also have given way to helicopters, which operate direct from the flat roof of a heliport in the centre of London's West End to similar heliports in the centre of Paris and every other big city within a radius of 300 miles, cutting out all tedious journeys between airports and city centres.

It all sounds rather fantastic, doesn't it? But so did jet-planes and atom-bombs a dozen years ago, and the prototypes of the 40-seat helicopters mentioned above are already being built in British factories. So are smaller helicopters for a host of different jobs, including a little two-seater that would make a fine family car of the air. Unfortunately, this is the only possibility that may never come to anything, for helicopters cost a lot of money to buy and to operate and they are, at the moment, more difficult to fly than ordinary fixed-wing aeroplanes. In any case, bearing in mind the accidents that happen to motor cars on our roads, it is perhaps just as well that everyone will not fly around in their own helicopters, as it is seldom possible to get out and argue whose fault it was after a collision in the air.

On the other hand, as short-range air liners and air 'buses, helicopters should be safer and better than anything else with wings. The great American inventor Thomas Elva Edison knew this as long ago as 1908 when he said "No aeroplane will be good until it can go straight up and down."

There were no jet-planes then. In fact, the world speed record for aeroplanes stood at only 32 m.p.h. But Edison already foresaw the dangers and difficulties that would be experienced one day when aircraft began to fly really fast.

That day has come and, instead of the slow speeds and short landing runs of 45 years ago, modern air liners approach their two-mile concrete runways at up to 120 m.p.h. Accidents are rare, thanks to the genius of our designers, skill of our pilots and uncanny radio and radar devices that can guide an air liner down to a safe landing at night or in bad weather when its pilot can see only his instruments. But the real answer to an airline operator's prayer is an aircraft that can fly fast and land slowly – and that means a helicopter, the only aircraft that can make its landing approach at one m.p.h. if its pilot wishes, or even hover motionless in the air.

Before going any further, it might be as well to learn just why a helicopter is able to do this, and how it differs from an Autogiro and a gyrodyne . . .

As you probably know, an aeroplane flies because, when it moves forward, air flows over its curved-section wings, producing sufficient "lift" to raise it from the ground. Obviously, the same thing happens if the aircraft stands still and its "wings" are turned through the air in the form of a helicopter rotor. In fact, enough lift can be produced to make it rise vertically from the ground without any forward run, and to fly safely at very low speeds. That is the principle of all rotating wing aircraft, and a very useful one, as it means they can take off and land in spaces little bigger than their rotor diameter, instead of needing hundreds of yards of expensive runway.

There are, however, important differences between the various types of rotating wing aircraft. Most early ones were helicopters; which is easy to understand as, on paper, they seem the simplest to design and build. Whereas an ordinary aeroplane needs wings to give it lift and a propeller to drive it forward, a helicopter's rotor combines both jobs in one. It turns fast enough to keep the helicopter airborne without any forward speed, and by tilting it the pilot can steer his aircraft in any direction he wishes. When the rotor is tilted forward the helicopter is propelled forward: and it can just as easily be made to fly sideways or even backwards, as well as vertically up and down.

Unfortunately, in the early days of flying, nobody really understood the mechanical and aerodynamic problems involved in building helicopters, so it is just as well that there were no engines of the right type or power to make any of them work. Sometimes helicopters managed to lift themselves a few feet into the air, tethered at the end of a piece of rope, but that was all. Certainly, none of them ever flew properly with anybody aboard. Then a brilliant Spanish inventor named Juan de la Cierva tackled the whole business from a new angle. He believed that the best and simplest answer was to take an ordinary aeroplane and replace its fixed wings with wings that would rotate automatically in the air, like the sails of a windmill.

He bought an old Avro 504 biplane and replaced its wings with a four-bladed rotor, naming the result an Autogiro. It worked beautifully. At any speed over 30 m.p.h. the rotor developed sufficient lift to keep the machine airborne. Below that speed the rotor still turned, but more slowly, and the Autogiro "glided" down to a safe, slow landing.

Chief drawback was that, although the rotor could be started by hand, it would not turn automatically in the airflow (or auto-rotate, as this is technically known) and produce sufficient lift for take-off until the aircraft was taxied along the ground. Thus, although the Autogiro took off and landed in a shorter distance than a comparable fixed-wing aeroplane and could fly slowly, it was still unable to fulfil Edison's 1908 formula for "a good aeroplane" that would go straight up and down.

Cierva's British company came near to success by fitting a clutch, so that the rotor could be turned by the engine until it produced sufficient lift to jump the aircraft off the ground. As soon as this happened, the clutch had to be disengaged and full power put into the propeller for forward flight, with the rotor wind-milling in the airflow.

It worked quite well, and Autogiros were used during the war for radar calibration duties, their slow-flying qualities making them ideal for such exacting work. Some are still flying, both in the United Kingdom and in Sweden, where a company named Helikopter-Flyg has completed many thousands of hours flying with Cierva C.30's, on everything from air taxi work to army co-operation and air ambulance duties.

Unfortunately, jump starts would seldom be appreciated by dear old ladies making their first flight, and the only real solution to the vertical take-off requirement is a helicopter. So, despite all the problems involved, designers continued trying to perfect an aircraft of this type, without much success until Igor Sikorsky built a weird contraption called the VS-300 in 1939.

It was not Sikorsky's first attempt to build a helicopter. Way back in 1908, in Russia, he had produced what looked like an iron bedstead surmounted by two butterfly-wing rotors. This managed to raise itself from the ground, but not with Sikorsky aboard. So he decided that the day of the helicopter had not arrived, and went on to build instead the world's first successful four-engined aeroplane.

Being a loyal Czarist, he fled from Russia after the Communist revolution, and eventually made a name for himself with superb amphibian and flying boat air liners which he designed and built for Pan American

Airways. But he never quite forgot his early dream of making a successful helicopter and, in the late 1930's, United Aircraft Corporation, who had taken over Sikorsky's factory, decided to let him have another shot at designing and building one.

It was no by means a hopeless gamble, as the Focke-Achgelis Fa.61 twin-rotor helicopter had already been demonstrated with fair success in Germany and the French pioneer, Louis Breguet, had also made short flights in a helicopter of his own design. Nevertheless, it was Sikorsky who put the helicopter right on the aeronautical map and his is still the greatest name in helicopter engineering.

The VS-300 was no thing of beauty. In its earliest form it consisted of a fabric-covered cockpit surmounted by a single big rotor and followed by a trellis-work rear fuselage carrying two more small horizontal rotors on outriggers and a vertical one to counteract torque (a tendency to make the whole aircraft spin round in the opposite direction to the main rotor). There was little doubt that Sikorsky had produced a winner. Unlike previous helicopters, his VS-300 did not try to shake itself to pieces, could fly fairly high and in a straight steady line. Its controls were so good that Sikorsky was even able to pick up a four inch ring from the top of a pole with a spike fixed to the helicopter's nose.

The U.S. Army lost no time in ordering a batch of Sikorsky helicopters to test their usefulness for ambulance, message-carrying, cable-laying, artillery observation, and other military duties. The U.S. Navy bought some for experimental flying from merchant ships, in the hope that they would be able to detect and destroy submarines. Even our own Royal Air Force ordered some.

Unknown to us at the time, the Germans too had decided to go in for helicopters in a big way. The Focke-Achgelis Fa.61 had been developed into the big twin-rotor Fa.223, designed to lift loads of up to $1\frac{1}{4}$ tons or to fly for several hours over the sea on mine-laying, anti-submarine or rescue duties. Despite its size, the Germans planned to build no fewer than 400 of these helicopters a month, but R.A.F. Bomber Command and the U.S. bomber fleets put a stop to all that and the Fa. 223 never went into action.

An even more startling German wartime helicopter project was a Focke-Wulf jet-fighter designed to fly at speeds up to 620 m.p.h. It was very different to helicopters as we know them. Instead of the usual "horizontal" rotor, it had a three-bladed, jet-propelled rotor which spun around its fuselage like a huge propeller behind, instead of in front of its cockpit.

Bearing in mind that the present world speed record for helicopters is only 129.5 m.p.h., and that few jets currently in service fly over 600 m.p.h., the Focke-Wulf would obviously have been some aircraft if the Germans had had the chance to build it in 1945. Fortunately they didn't, but several companies in both Britain and America have seriously considered helicopter fighters of this type since the war.

Naturally, such a design would be no use for a passenger-carrying helicopter, because the only way to get

take-off vertically but change into ordinary fixed-wing aircraft for cruising flight.

Convertoplane designs are many and varied, ranging from aeroplanes with folding rotors to hybrids with big swivelling propellers that are horizontal like a helicopter rotor for take-off and move into a normal vertical position once the aircraft reaches a safe height. Unfortunately, nobody seems to know what will happen while they are being swung down!

A more logical step towards higher speed, because it

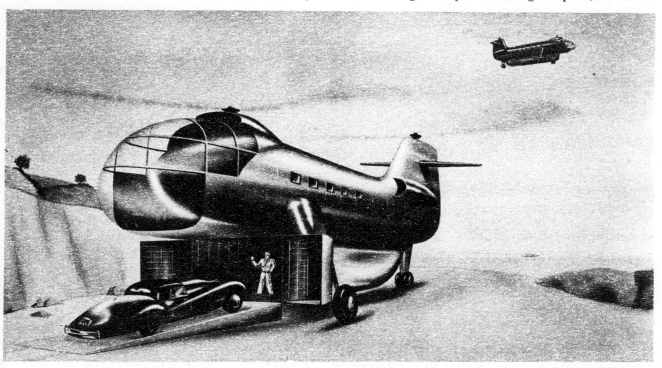

How Silver City Airways may ferry cars across the Channel in a few years time.

it off the ground would be to stand its fuselage on end so that it could shoot off vertically. Nevertheless, it is important to try and find ways of increasing the speed of helicopters, because no helicopter yet built is able to fly as fast as the 18-year-old Dakota transport aeroplane.

This is not quite as serious as it sounds, because the coach journey from the centre of London to London Airport takes at least half an hour and so does the journey from Orly Airport to the centre of Paris. Thus, a helicopter passenger making a direct flight from city-centre to city-centre at 150 m.p.h. would arrive before a passenger who made the trip aboard two coaches and a 250 m.p.h. air liner. But military transport services in particular are anxious to find a way of combining the high cruising speed of a fixed-wing aircraft with the slow-flying qualities of a helicopter. The result has been a growing interest in convertoplanes – aircraft able to

also offers improved safety, is the gyrodyne, pioneered since the war by the British Fairey Aviation Company. This combines the best features of a helicopter and an Autogiro, as, although its main rotor is engine-driven, it is used only to provide lift. The aircraft is driven forward by an ordinary propeller, which also counters torque set up by the main rotor, so eliminating need for the usual tail rotor.

First aircraft of this type was the four-seat Fairey Gyrodyne of 1947, which had a single 500 h.p. Leonides engine to drive its rotor and propeller. Although it had no more power than any other four-seater, the Gyrodyne was nearly 50 per cent faster than comparable helicopters of that time, and a British speed record which it set up in 1948 has still not been beaten.

Now Fairey's have gone one important stage further by replacing the Gyrodyne's original three-bladed engine-driven rotor with a two-bladed jet-rotor, driven by small powerful pressure-jets at each blade-tip. Such a rotor produces no torque. As a result, the full power of the Gyrodyne's engine can be put into its two propellers, giving even higher forward speeds.

The jet-Gyrodyne is, however, little more than a small-scale flying model of the big 40-seat Rotodyne, which should be flying within a year or two, and which will almost certainly be the fastest helicopter and safest aircraft of any kind in the world. It could almost be called a convertoplane, because it looks and flies like an ordinary fixed-wing aeroplane, but has a big five-bladed rotor in addition to small fixed wings.

For take-off, powerful jet-engines mounted above its fuselage will send compressed air through the hollow rotor-blades to pressure jets at the tips, enabling the Rotodyne to take off vertically from any 90 ft. square field, town square or factory roof. Once airborne, the gas-turbines will gradually divert their thrust from the rotor to two propeller-turbines mounted on the aircraft's fixed wings, building up to a maximum forward cruising speed of 200 m.p.h. – nearly double the speed of present-day helicopters. After that, the Rotodyne will be able to fly as an Autogiro, with its rotor auto-rotating; or as a helicopter; or as a gyrodyne with power shared between its rotor and propellers.

Should one of its gas-turbines fail during vertical take-off or one of its propeller-turbines stop during cruising flight, it will maintain height on the remaining units. If all its engines stopped together, its rotor would continue to auto-rotate and "glide" it down to a safe landing. Even if it lost a rotor blade, it would still have sufficient fixed wing area to make a comparatively safe, if fast, landing. No other helicopter offers such safety.

UNFORTUNATELY, the Rotodyne will not be flying for some time. Meanwhile, how good are the helicopters of today?

Firstly we must decide what we mean by "good". If we mean "do they work?" the answer is "yes". In Korea a squadron of twelve Sikorsky S-55's carried an entire battalion of 1,000 Marines to the front line in four hours – an operation that would have taken 6½ hours using 100 army lorries. Others lifted 260 Marines to an otherwise inaccessible mountain position, and laid telephone cable to link the troops with their H.Q. as they went. A succession of such missions convinced U.S. Army authorities of the unrivalled value of helicopters as military transports, and they plan to spend some £178 millions to replace lorries with helicopters over the next year or so.

On the other hand, if we mean "are helicopters cheap to operate?" the answer is an equally firm "no". A small helicopter costs anything up to £30,000 initially and £25 an hour to operate, and no airline could afford to use such machines permanently for passenger or cargo-carrying. Not until bigger helicopters, able to carry about 20 passengers, become available will they begin to make a profit, and even then it will be small.

But the all-important fact to remember is that helicopters can do jobs beyond the capabilities of any fixed-wing aeroplane or surface vehicle ever built. Lifting troops up a mountain under fire is almost commonplace compared with the achievement of a Sikorsky S.51 which carried food to the marooned 'keepers of Wolf Rock lighthouse during a gale, or others which land regularly in tiny jungle clearings in Malaya to lift to safety badly-wounded soldiers of Britain's Far Eastern armies.

THE idea of flying a helicopter to and fro over orchards, to beat raindrops from cherries with the rotor "downwash" after a heavy storm, might seem little more than a stunt. But if the sun had caused those rain-soaked cherries to swell and burst, the farmers would have lost over £60,000.

It is impossible to give a list of all the jobs that a helicopter can do, because new ones are being found almost daily. They have been used for pipe and cable-laying, for electric grid inspection, geological survey, for keeping track of herds of cattle, shooting film sequences, fire-fighting and chasing escaped convicts. Many lives have been saved by helicopters, including passengers from aircraft wrecked in the Arctic, in the swampy forests of Newfoundland and the tropical jungles of Brazil. "Ditched" aircrews have been snatched from the sea; locust swarms have been sprayed with insecticide and killed in the Argentine; and crops dusted with pest-killer in almost every country in the world.

The U.S. Marine Corps, having proved the value of helicopter transports in Korea, plans to use its bigger Piasecki twin-rotor helicopters as beach assault transports, replacing the invasion barges of World War II. By flying from dispersed aircraft carriers, they believe they could achieve surprise by landing in the enemy's rear, and far better concentration of strength than if they were dropped by parachute or glider. Nor would they have to go into action lightly-armed, for the Piasecki H.21 Work-Horse can carry a 75 mm. field gun slung under its banana-shaped fuselage, and big

The Piasecki helicopter is able to carry a field gun under its fuselage.

helicopters now under development could carry easily bigger guns, jeeps or even light tanks.

At the other end of the military scale, firms like McDonnell and Hiller are building tiny jet-powered helicopters that may well replace light aircraft and motor cycles for military reconnaissance, spotting and despatch carrying.

Money spent by the Services on these military helicopters will speed development of new civil helicopters. British European Airways have already given a glimpse of future possibilities by operating successfully the world's first helicopter passenger and night mail services, achieving incredibly high regularity in all weathers. This is another important advantage of helicopters. If he runs into a heavy storm, a helicopter pilot can feel his way along gingerly at a few miles an hour, or even squat in a convenient open space until the air has cleared. Such safety features will undoubtedly endear helicopters to the travelling public in due course and, whatever their present limitations, it seems inevitable that helicopters will one day replace fixed-wing air

liners on most airline routes up to 300 miles in length.

Britain's cross-channel car ferry operators, Silver City Airways, have already had the courage to announce that they plan to replace their Bristol Freighters with big helicopters in a few years time; and Fairey's have stated that the Rotodyne will, if required, carry three small cars instead of the usual 40 passengers. Bristols have their 13-seat Type 173 ready for air 'bus service, and bigger helicopters on the way. Saunders-Roe have in the two-seat Skeeter an excellent helicopter trainer and the nearest thing yet to a flying family car.

But, even bearing in mind past predictions that motor cars would never replace stage coaches, we still dare to predict that the day will never come when every family will own a helicopter or, for that matter, any other form of aircraft. On the other hand, it may not be many years before we catch the 8.20 Rotodyne to town or fly to France with our motor cars in similar aircraft; for there is no doubt whatsoever that the air 'buses are coming, and that they will have rotating wings.

WENCESLAS THE GOOD

STORY BY R.B. SAXE
DRAWN BY Norman Williams

In the early tenth century Wratislas I was King of Bohemia. He had two sons, Wenceslas and Boleslas. Wenceslas was brought up mainly by his grandmother, the good and pious Ludmila.

I AM SO GLAD YOU LOVE YOUR BIBLE, WENCESLAS. MANY OF OUR PEOPLE ARE STILL PAGANS. WHEN YOU ARE KING YOU MUST CONVERT THEM.

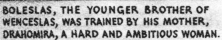

BOLESLAS, THE YOUNGER BROTHER OF WENCESLAS, WAS TRAINED BY HIS MOTHER, DRAHOMIRA, A HARD AND AMBITIOUS WOMAN.

YOU MUST PRACTISE WITH EVERY WEAPON, BOLESLAS. FIGHTING IS THE ONLY PROFESSION FOR A PRINCE.

IN 926, WRATISLAS DIES

NOW I AM KING, MOTHER, I WILL BUILD MORE CHURCHES, AND CONVERT ALL OUR PEOPLE TO THE CHRISTIAN FAITH.

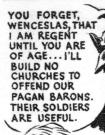

YOU FORGET, WENCESLAS, THAT I AM REGENT UNTIL YOU ARE OF AGE... I'LL BUILD NO CHURCHES TO OFFEND OUR PAGAN BARONS. THEIR SOLDIERS ARE USEFUL.

LISTEN, MY BARONS. THE ELBE STATES ARE MAKING RAIDS INTO THE GERMAN EMPIRE. WE MUST JOIN IN AND GET OUR SHARE OF PLUNDER.

LED BY PRINCE BOLESLAS, THE RAIDS BEGIN.

A MOST SUCCESSFUL RAID, MOTHER. WE BROUGHT BACK CATTLE, GOLD AND JEWELS.

YOU MUST STOP THESE RAIDS, MOTHER. HENRY OF GERMANY IS VERY STRONG. HE'LL ATTACK US... THERE WILL BE MUCH SLAUGHTER!

IF HE DOES ATTACK US, OUR NEIGHBOURING STATES WILL JOIN IN ... THEN HE'LL HAVE HIS HANDS FULL.

THE FOLLOWING DAY

GRAVE NEWS, YOUR MAJESTY. HENRY HAS CROSSED THE BORDER AND IS ADVANCING ON PRAGUE UNOPPOSED.

YOU HEARD, MOTHER, UNOPPOSED. WHERE ARE THE OTHER STATES YOU SAID WOULD HELP US?

THEY WILL. WE WILL DEFEND PRAGUE.

WHAT CAN I DO TO STOP THIS EVIL WAR? IF ONLY MY GRANDMOTHER WERE ALIVE SHE COULD ADVISE ME.

THE GERMANS! A MIGHTY HOST! WE'RE DONE FOR!

YOU MUST MAKE TERMS WITH HENRY AT ONCE, MOTHER, BEFORE THE FIGHTING STARTS.

WHAT! AND BE SERFS FOR THE REST OF OUR LIVES?

THEN WENCESLAS MAKES A GREAT DECISION

LISTEN, MY CAPTAINS! I AM ABOLISHING THE REGENCY AND SEIZING POWER FROM THIS MOMENT. GIVE ME A HORSE. I WILL RIDE TO HENRY MYSELF

OPEN THE GATE! DO YOU HEAR? I AM YOUR KING!

THE CAMP OF KING HENRY

LOOK, YOUR MAJESTY! A MESSENGER RIDING TOWARDS US.

BRING HIM TO ME.

YOUR MAJESTY, I AM KING WENCESLAS. I HAVE ABOLISHED THE REGENCY AND SEIZED POWER. I CRAVE A FAIR AND HONOURABLE PEACE

THOSE ARE BRAVE WORDS. COME TO MY PAVILION AND WE WILL TRY TO SETTLE THIS LITTLE MATTER

YOU WILL FORM PART OF MY EMPIRE, OF COURSE. IN RETURN, I GUARANTEE YOU PEACE, AND YOU MUST PAY A YEARLY TRIBUTE OF 500 PIECES OF SILVER AND 120 OXEN

YOUR TERMS ARE GENEROUS. I WILL SIGN THE TREATY NOW

PEACE! I BRING PEACE

HURRAH FOR WENCESLAS

HURRAH!

MOTHER! HENRY GUARANTEES US PEACE. NOW I CAN BUILD CHURCHES AND CONVERT OUR BACKWARD SUBJECTS

A LOT OF THE BARONS ARE PAGANS. IF YOU TRY TO CONVERT THEIR SERFS THEY'LL REBEL

THE BARONS THEMSELVES WILL BE CONVERTED IN TIME

AND THE FIRST CHURCH WENCESLAS BUILT WAS THAT OF ST. VITUS, IN PRAGUE

CHURCHES! SCHOOLS! EVERYTHING FOR THE PEOPLE. IF ONLY YOU WERE KING, BOLESLAS, HOW DIFFERENT THINGS WOULD BE.

BUT HIS MOTHER AND BROTHER PLOT AGAINST WENCESLAS.

I'M ONLY THE GOVERNOR OF A SMALL PROVINCE WITHOUT A SAY IN ANYTHING! I THINK I'LL HAVE A TALK WITH THE BARONS

IF WENCESLAS TRIES TO CONVERT MY SERFS INTO REBELLIOUS DOGS OF CHRISTIANS, HE'LL BE ASKING FOR TROUBLE.

YES, AND HE'LL GET IT

YOU HAVE BEEN SPECIALLY TRAINED TO GO INTO THE BACKWARD PARTS OF OUR COUNTRY AND PREACH THE GOSPEL. THERE ARE NO CHURCHES THERE SO YOU MUST WORK WHERE YOU CAN

BUT WENCESLAS CONTINUES TO SEND OUT MISSIONARIES TO CONVERT THE PEOPLE.

YOU WILL PROBABLY GET SOME OPPOSITION FROM THE BARONS, SO YOUR TASK WILL NOT BE EASY.

WE KNOW THE DIFFICULTIES, SIRE, AND WE GRATEFULLY THANK YOU FOR SELECTING US FOR SO IMPORTANT A MISSION. GOD WILL HELP US

I KNOW YOUR LOT IS HARD, MY BROTHERS, BUT YOU MUST NOT REBEL AGAINST YOUR MASTERS. ONE DAY, WHEN THEY TOO SEE THE LIGHT —

THE BARON'S SOLDIERS! RUN FOR YOUR LIVES!

COME WITH ME, BROTHER. I WILL HIDE YOU.

WE ARE PERSECUTED, AND SO WE MUST WORSHIP SECRETLY IN THIS POOR BARN

THE MISSONARIES AND THEIR CONVERTS ARE DRIVEN INTO HIDING....

BUT GOD WILL NOT MIND THAT. REMEMBER THAT OUR LORD HIMSELF WAS BORN IN A MANGER.

BACK IN THE PALACE

IT IS TIME FOR ME TO GIVE ALMS TO THE POOR. BRING THOSE SMALL BAGS OF MONEY, PAGE.

YES, SIRE.

HERE, YOU POOR WOMAN, TAKE THIS MONEY AND MAY GOD BE WITH YOU

GOD BLESS YOU, YOUR MAJESTY ...MAY HE KEEP AND PROTECT YOU.

WENCESLAS IS NOW TWENTY-SEVEN AND STILL HAS THESE SILLY IDEAS OF ALMS GIVING AND SO ON EVERY DAY. OUR SERFS ARE ASKING FOR MORE. IT'S INTOLERABLE!

ONE DAY - IN THE YEAR 936....

WE MUST GET TOGETHER AND DO SOMETHING NOW! BOLESLAS IS ON OUR SIDE. HE'D MAKE THE SORT OF KING WE WANT.

TO-DAY IS THE FEAST OF ST. STEPHEN, STANISLAS.

YES, SIRE. AND BITTER COLD OUTSIDE

LOOK AT THAT POOR OLD MAN GATHERING TWIGS! DO YOU KNOW WHERE HE LIVES?

YES, SIRE, A GOOD LEAGUE AWAY.

BRING FOOD AND A LARGE BUNDLE OF FAGGOTS WE'LL MAKE THE OLD FELLOW HAPPY TO-NIGHT

I WILL, SIRE

IT IS VERY COLD, SIRE, AND I AM TIRED. I CANNOT GO ON MUCH FURTHER.

BE STRONG, MY BOY. OUR PURPOSE IS GOOD ~ TAKE FRESH HEART AND CARRY ON.

THERE'S THE COTTAGE, STANISLAS. NOW WE SHAN'T BE LONG.

HERE WE ARE AT LAST, AND YOU'RE WARMER NOW, AREN'T YOU?

THE KING!

YES, MY FRIEND; COME WITH GIFTS TO WISH YOU GOOD CHEER

HOW CAN I EVER REPAY YOU, SIRE?

GOOD-BYE...I AM WELL REWARDED BY YOUR HAPPINESS, MY FRIEND.

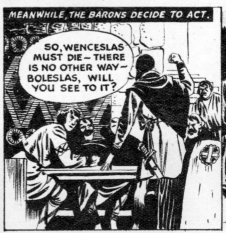

MEANWHILE, THE BARONS DECIDE TO ACT.

SO, WENCESLAS MUST DIE ~ THERE IS NO OTHER WAY ~ BOLESLAS, WILL YOU SEE TO IT?

HE IS MY BROTHER BUT.....IT MUST BE DONE.

MOTHER, THE BARONS HAVE DECREED THAT WENCESLAS MUST DIE.

IF IT IS THE ONLY WAY, THEN I MUST RESIGN MYSELF TO IT.

TO-MORROW MORNING THE KING GOES TO CHURCH AT ALTBUNZLAU. WE WILL WAYLAY HIM~ AND STRIKE!

THE MORNING OF 28TH SEPTEMBER, 926 A.D.

HERE HE COMES!

GOOD MORNING, BROTHER.

I'VE A WARMER GREETING FOR YOU!

GOD FORGIVE THEE BROTHER.

HE IS DEAD, MY LORD. I KILLED HIM.

AND WENCESLAS THE BELOVED WAS CARRIED INTO THE CHURCH OF ST. VITUS, THERE TO LIE IN STATE AND BE HONOURED BY HIS LOVING SUBJECTS.

936 A.D. WENCESLAS WAS 27.

BOLESLAS WAS NOW KING, BUT IT BROUGHT HIM NO JOY AFTER THE DREADFUL THING HE HAD DONE. FULL OF REMORSE HE GAVE HIS YOUNG SON STRACHKWAS TO THE CHURCH AS AN ACT OF REPENTANCE.

Thus died King Wenceslas, Saint and Martyr. ~~~~ So great was his example in that violent and turbulent age that his fame spread to all lands, and to this day, all over the world, he is remembered and sung of at ~~~~ Christmastide

THE CAPTAIN'S JOB

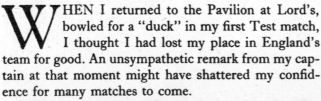

Stories and Hints about cricket's
most responsible position
written by LEN HUTTON

ILLUSTRATED BY GERALD LIPMAN

WHEN I returned to the Pavilion at Lord's, bowled for a "duck" in my first Test match, I thought I had lost my place in England's team for good. An unsympathetic remark from my captain at that moment might have shattered my confidence for many matches to come.

But what R. W. V. Robins said to me was: "For goodness' sake, Len, don't do that against the Aussies next year!"

It was a shrewd and understanding action on the part of my skipper, who came to my rescue in the only way possible during one of the blackest moments of my cricketing career, and it taught me the value of a captain who has studied the character and capabilities of each man in his team. Believe me, that knowledge is essential to the captain who hopes to get the best out of his players.

Actually, I've been lucky in all the captains I have had, and I've tried to profit from their example. I'll try to pass on to you some of the lessons I have learned.

I owe a great deal to Colonel Chichester-Constable,

my first skipper, when I played in the Minor Counties Championship at the age of seventeen. At a time when I was raw and inexperienced, needing every bit of help and advice, my skipper never failed me.

The other players, no less, appreciated his encouragement. We developed a respect for him, a confidence in each others' ability, a will to win and, in consequence, a team spirit that turned us into a crack eleven.

The lesson I learned from this experience was that "it is better to have a lion at the head of an army of sheep, than a sheep at the head of an army of lions". With our good skipper even we inexperienced sheep played like lions.

In due course I was able to earn a place in the Yorkshire county side where I had the advantage of the skilful leadership and the personal encouragement of Brian Sellers, a cricketer who believed that a game is never lost until it is won, and set a fine example of grit and determination when the odds were against us.

If my first county captain had a fault it was one over which he had no control, because it was a matter of luck. The fact was, however, that Brian Sellers just couldn't win the toss, and thus failed to perform his first task on the field efficiently! In one season alone, I remember, he lost the toss thirteen times in succession. Whatever did Sir Pelham Warner think about that? For it was Sir Pelham who, after praising the late Sir Stanley Jackson's ability to make runs in Test matches, added dryly; "Jacker was a good tosser".

In fact Sir Stanley won the toss five times out of five in the Test match series of 1905. He led one of the most successful of all England teams against Australia, proving that even the best skippers can make good use of a little luck. Unfortunately, however, all the practice in the world will not enable you to improve your ability in this respect.

Incidentally, Sir Pelham Warner was himself a famous captain, not idly dubbed "The General". A General, it has been said, is "a man who has his men behind him before the battle and ahead of him during it". But Sir Pelham did not conform to this pattern. He led his teams "into battle" and inspired them by personal example.

Wally Hammond, my England skipper for seventeen of the Test matches in which I have played, was a leader in the same mould. He never asked any of us to do something he could not do himself, for he was a master in every department of the game. That, to my mind, is the best qualification a captain can have.

So – if you have been honoured with the captaincy of your team, or if you have ambitions in that direction – take this advice from me. Practice to improve your own ability – make sure that you are worthy of your place in the team as a player as well as a captain. I tell you this for your own sakes, because you will find it a heartbreaking job trying to lead a team to victory when you are yourself a weak link in that team.

Confident in your own ability as a cricketer, possessing an intimate knowledge of the character and ability of each member of your team, and ready to lead them like a lion into battle, you need not fear the task ahead, no matter what circumstances arise.

That "circumstances will arise" you can be certain, for there never was a game of cricket exactly the same as another before it. Each one contains unexpected situations calling for instantaneous decisions on your part. Think each situation out carefully – make a firm, confident decision in each case, and stick to it! No one can do better than that.

Before going out for the toss you should inspect the wicket, take advice about the weather, weigh up the characteristics of your opponents and their strength against that of your own team, and form an opinion

about what kind of general tactics will be necessary to win the match. With regard to the pitch, remember that hard soil is likely to favour fast bowling; heavier soil, after rain, may aid your spin bowlers, while a "green" wicket will help those bowlers who can make the ball fizz and turn.

All right! You've won the toss. Now for your first decision, and you must choose wisely in order to preserve the advantage. To bat, or not to bat?

If you are still in doubt, and especially if you are

Len Hutton leading an England eleven on to the field.

playing a one-day match, my advice is – bat first. This always gives you the opportunity to gain the initiative and to dictate the terms under which the game is to be played.

Who is going to open your batting? I recommend you to start with your soundest men. Their job is to stay at the wicket until they have established dominance over the bowling.

Do not worry if runs are slow to come at first. If the openers play each ball on its merits, but refrain from nibbling at those tempting early balls wide of the stumps, runs will come steadily and your innings will be given a firm foundation. After that you can send in your hitters to press home the advantage and force the pace if necessary.

But the best laid plans have a habit of going astray, so don't be afraid to change the batting order to stop a collapse. Sometimes the introduction of a left-handed batsman will stop the kind of rot a leg-break bowler likes to create. It's also a good plan to arrange for a left-handed batsman to be in at the same time as a right-hander. This not only upsets a bowler, but his fieldsmen as well, for they are necessarily changing position very frequently while the left-hander is in.

WHEN your best batsman fails to make a good score, neither you nor he is going to be very pleased about it. Cricket, as Thomas Hood discovered, is most trying to the temper, for a player cannot lose his wicket without being put out. It may be that the batsman was out through sheer bad luck, or he may have committed the very fault you had warned him against. In either case, if you know your man, you should know the right thing to say to inspire him to do better next time.

With some chaps a word of commiseration will do the trick; with others nothing short of a good wigging will bring a response. You must be prepared to deliver either with authority.

When your side is batting, in a sense each man is his own captain. Under normal circumstances he should be allowed to play his natural game, and you should only give such instructions as: "keep your end up at all costs", or "speed it up" if those tactics are essential to the overall plan. When you do give them, make sure they are understood and obeyed.

Be careful about declarations. It isn't only the number of runs to be made that you must take into consideration, but the probable rate of scoring. It's surprising how quickly a side can knock up a hundred runs when time is the enemy!

The captain of the side which is about to bat is usually asked which roller he wishes to be used. To obtain the best batting conditions I generally plump for the light roller if there is a chance of the pitch crumbling, but if it is soft, and cut up, then I ask for the full seven minutes with the heavy roller. There is no need to worry if you are called upon to decide this question, for, as you can see, it's just a matter of common sense.

But now you are about to take the field, and this is where your main job as captain begins.

First, make sure that your team look smart and businesslike and, of course, you must set the example in this respect, too. Nothing gives a side more confidence than to know that they are well turned-out, with clean flannels and shirts, and well-spiked boots.

You'll need all the confidence you can muster, too, because you are the General who is about to launch his attack.

New batsmen are bound to be a bit uncertain in their stroke play at first, so start with your most dangerous bowlers and set an intimidating field. Attack every new batsman in this way before he gets settled. If you have watched international or county cricket you will have noticed how faithfully we obey that principle. Every time a wicket falls the field moves in close to the new batsman, no matter how widely scattered it was before his arrival.

It's usually best to open with your fast bowlers while they are fresh. Their speed will allow the batsmen less time to think, and if you are lucky enough to have the use of a new ball then your pace bowlers can take advantage of the shine on it to make it swing in the air. And when the shine has worn off your spinners will be able to get a better grip on the ball to perform their particular skills.

It is part of your job to help your bowlers to set their field and, needless to say, to see that every man knows his place and is on his toes ready for that early catch you are hoping for. Many a game, and many a championship has been won by alert fieldsmen, and each fielder should have a role in the tactical plan which is under your control.

You will know the ability of your men in the field. Those with safe hands and lightning anticipation will have been allotted such specialist positions as slips, cover point and short leg. They are there to give your bowlers additional confidence.

COMPLICATED instructions on the field of play should be quite unnecessary. You should have drilled your men at practice so that a wave, or nod of the head, is enough indication to a fieldsman that he is to move nearer, deeper or to one side, according to the signals you have arranged. You have enough to do without having to go into detailed orders once the play has begun.

For instance, you must study the incoming batsmen and the effect your bowling is having upon them. Stop them from playing their natural game if you can.

This man grips the bat near the top of the handle. Almost certainly he's a hitter in front of the wicket. You might decide to feed him with chances to make his favourite strokes and tempt him into error before his eye is in; if he's too strong, however, you must be able to block those strokes just as effectively.

The other chap has a low grip – looks like a hooker.

Len Hutton making a sweep to leg.

your pace men will not be able to manage more than four or five overs comfortably in their opening spell. But don't make changes unnecessarily. Don't take Tom off just because poor old Jim is getting cold in the out-field, and gets niggley if he's not asked to bowl.

A good captain shows neither fear nor favour. His one consideration is "what is best for the team" and his one aim: Victory.

Be the Boss. Take a firm line with the slackers, and, once you have given your decision, do not allow other members of the team to attempt to over-rule you, or to question your authority. But before giving a decision, don't neglect to consult your bowlers, your wicket-keeper, and other experienced members of the team when you feel it advantageous to do so. Two heads are better than one in many cases, and often your colleagues will spot things that you would not otherwise have known about from your own position in the field.

The wicket-keeper can be particularly valuable to you for he has a close-up view of every ball that is bowled. Indeed I have often thought that in many respects the man behind the stumps is in an ideal position to captain the side himself.

On the other hand, it is said that a specialist bowler is not in a good position to act as skipper, because he is often doubtful as to when to put himself on to bowl and when to take himself off. Yet I have known many fine bowler-captains whose judgment in this respect could not be criticised. So when a captain is being chosen I would say that the all-important question must be: who is the best man for the job? If there is an outstanding candidate then no other consideration should prevent his selection.

There is one other piece of advice I want to give you about captaincy: try every trick you know in order to get wickets, but play fair. You, more than any other member of the team, should know the rules inside out, should keep to the spirit of them and see that your men do, too. Don't allow wild appeals, even if they are made only out of keenness and the very enthusiasm that you are anxious to foster. Only the wicket-keeper, or bowler, is really in a position to judge whether a batsman can be given out L.B.W., for instance, and they are the only ones who should be allowed to appeal.

Take the umpire's decision as final, whichever way it goes. Umpires have been known to make mistakes, but you gain nothing by pointing this out on the field. Get on with the game and better luck will surely follow.

A good captain needs patience, courage and tact in large quantities, and there is one other quality that I regard as indispensable – a sense of humour! Why ? – because a happy team is invariably a successful one.

All right – let your bowlers attack him on the off, where his particular grip will give him little scope. A good leg-break bowler may persuade the batsman to play against the spin. All these things you must consider.

Keep the initiative at all costs. If a batsman shows signs of settling down change your field around, set a trap for him, change your bowling in the way that will worry him most. Never relax concentration for an instant.

You'll know the strength of your bowlers. Probably

PUZZLE CORNER by HUBERT PHILLIPS

1. WEIGHTS

I have a pair of scales and three weights, and with these three weights I can weigh any number of pounds from 1 up to 13. (I may, of course, find it necessary to put one or more weights in both scales.)

What are my three weights?

2. SIX VOWELS

"Money doesn't grow on trees," said a friend of mine . . . "So I suppose I must start living . . ."
Each of the missing words contains, in their proper order, the six vowels a, e, i, o, u, y.

What words are they?

3. ACCOUNT RENDERED

I have to pay a bill for 1s 1d.

How can I pay it with two coins, of which one must not be a shilling?

4. FAMOUS ENGLISHMEN

These are anagrams of the names of five famous Englishmen, i.e. the letters of each name have been shuffled.

What names are they?

1. SONNEL. 2. MEWCROLL. 3. HRILCCUHL. 4. SPEAKHEARSE. 5. HURBALGROOM.

5. JACK AND BILL

Jack and Bill are keen long-distance runners. One day they arranged a competition on the road – a perfectly flat road – which runs from Greystoke to Redhill. Jack started at the first milestone from Greystoke, and Bill at the twelfth milestone, and they ran to meet one another. Jack arrived at the sixth milestone two minutes before Bill.

Who is the better runner?

6. ANISEED

Messrs Aniseed, Bismuth and Carboy each own a horse. Each has named his horse after one of the others. In a recent race each rode the horse which was neither his own property nor his own namesake. Mr Aniseed rode the horse Carboy.

Who owns the horse Aniseed?

1	2	3	4	5
6				
7				
8				
9				

7. WORD SQUARE

This is rather an odd crossword, because the answers to the five "across" clues are the same as the answers to the five "down" clues. In other words, it is a word square.

CLUES

1 AC and 1 DN. The ebb and flow
6 AC and 2 DN. Empty
7 AC and 3 DN. Italy's greatest poet
8 AC and 4 DN. Come in, please
9 AC and 5 DN. Prophets

8. SUBSCRIPTION

The members of a class subscribed for a present to their master. Everyone handed in his contribution in pennies, and all gave the same amount. Contributions totalled 10s 1d.

How many subscribers were there?

9. THOUGHT FOR TODAY

"For today, this thought I give:
".. .. .."

Can you work out the second line? It consists, as you see, of twenty letters, which are AAEEIILLNNOORRSSTTVV, and it reads the same backwards as forwards.

10. JOSEPH AND JOSEPHINE

"Look, there's my niece," said Joseph to his sister Josephine. "Your niece, perhaps, but not mine," said Josephine.

How is this conversation to be explained?

11. BUGGINS

Buggins was applying for his first job. "The pay is £100 a year," said the manager, "rising by £20 annually. Or, alternatively, you can have £50 for the first six months, rising every six months by £5. Which you do prefer?" "The former, of course," said Buggins. "Then you don't get the job," said the manager. *Why not?*

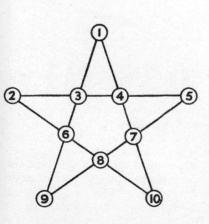

12. PENTACLE

Here is a "pentacle" puzzle. By substituting letters for numbers, you can produce seven words which have the following meanings:

1. 1 5 10 9 2 : ROUTES
2. 8 7 4 3 6 : WRONG-DOING
3. 5 4 3 2   : OBJECTS
4. 9 6 3 1   : FIBRE
5. 2 6 8 10   : FACTION
6. 5 7 8 9   : STRUCTURE
7. 10 7 4 1   : STUMBLE

WATCH OUT FOR THIS BEE

Have you ever noticed a rose-bush with semi-circular pieces cut out of its leaves? (1) You probably have, as it is quite a common sight, but what you may not have seen is the creature actually doing the cutting. This work is done by the Leaf-cutting Bee, known as a Solitary Bee, as it works alone. The Bee carries these pieces of leaf away (2) to form the "walls" of the bedrooms for the grubs. These bedrooms are constructed in tunnels bored in rotten wood, old earth-worm or beetle burrows or in tunnels specially dug in the ground (3). In picture (4) we show the cells completed in a tunnel in a tree trunk. Each cell is provided with pollen and honey and on this an egg is laid. Here–the pieces of leaf, each cut to the exact size required, having been glued together with a waxy substance – the grub hatches. It lives for a time on the food stored in its bedroom (5). This food is sufficient for it to become fully-grown. It then spins a cocoon (6) turns into a pupa and later emerges as a fully-developed bee (7).

Wings over the Ocean

The Men, Planes and Carriers that watch the Seas

WRITTEN AND ILLUSTRATED BY LAURENCE DUNN

ABOARD a minesweeper I had been watching their contribution to some recent NATO naval exercises. Then my imagination was stirred one day by the sight of Coastal Command Aircraft as they passed to and from their long distance ocean patrols. It had previously been arranged that I could transfer to other Naval Craft later on, but here was something much more interesting.

So it was that at 2 a.m. one morning – having obtained the necessary permission – I found myself in the Operations room of a Coastal Command Station listening to an air-crew being briefed. A vast wall map of the North Sea and Western Approaches, dotted with a variety of moveable symbols showed us the positions of our Convoys and warships and where "enemy" vessels had last been sighted.

Given our assignment – to patrol an area West of the Scillies and there maintain a CLA (creeping line ahead) as we searched for hostile craft – we next heard the Met. report and studied recognition drawings. Then by launch through the darkness to our Sunderland, one of several lying at moorings a short distance offshore. A little later we were taxi-ing down the still sleeping harbour to a clear stretch of water for our take-off.

Countless trawlers and other ships were sighted during the next twelve hours and I learned of the monotony and tedium which are inseparable from such routine patrols, also too of the excitement which comes with a "sighting" and how clearly even the slim snort of a submerged submarine can show on the radar screen. The Leigh Light and Sonar buoy are other devices too which have helped to make the patrolling aircraft a yet more deadly menace to the submarine.

How different was the next scene on the bridge of the "Implacable", 32,000 ton fleet carrier!

One of the outer screen of destroyers protecting our convoy had just picked up the "ping" of a submarine on her asdic. Immediately all was bustle as the carrier, with decks heeling turned sharply into the wind to fly off her aircraft. A minute later the first plane was airborne, the rest following amid a crescendo of noise at few seconds intervals. Astern, our attendant Battle class destroyer momentarily disappeared in spray, as following our course, she cut through the turmoil of our wake.

Such unison and understanding between seaman and airman has not come easily, but has only been achieved after years of slow and gradual development, hastened by war experience.

WHILE R.A.F. Coastal Command, with its Shackletons, Sunderlands, Neptunes etc. operating from fixed bases, is concerned only with ocean patrol, reconnaissance and anti-submarine duties, Naval Aviation with whom it works in closest co-operation, has the advantage of mobile bases, self-contained, and which can operate at short notice in any part of the globe and which, because of their separation from land, are proof against sabotage and infiltration.

When the name Fleet Air Arm was changed to Naval Aviation, the Navy showed that the air element had truly come into its own and had developed from being merely an auxiliary into a major integral part of the Service. So, too, in just over thirty years the Carrier has developed from scratch into the capital ship of the Navy, around which the rest of the fleet is built, just as in the past the fleet was built around the battleship.

The aircraft carrier has a dual personality. She has comparatively little armament; her strength lies in her planes and her worth as a fighting ship in her ability to get these up quickly and get them back again. In her there is a vast amount of power available, and Naval scientists, are always seeking new ways in which this may be used to increase general efficiency and the rate at which planes may be flown on and off.

One of the most important new British inventions is the steam catapult, now also being adopted by the U.S. Navy and known by the latter as the "hot ride". With it heavy high speed aircraft may be shot off, even

when the ship is stationary, obviating the need to steam into the wind. Complementary to the steam catapult is the angled deck of the carriers, allowing a plane to fly straight off the side of the ship, should its landing hook fail to engage the arrester wires. To land on the flight deck an aircraft now approaches from dead astern, touching down on the after part of the deck, where it should be held by arrester wires. Beyond these are barriers to stop any plane which may overshoot the wires. Now these barriers may be eliminated. An aircraft about to land will approach the ship from the starboard side at an angle of about 8 degrees. With no barrier ahead it can, if necessary, take off again over the port side of the carrier for another attempt. This diagonal layout has the effect of lengthening the carrier by 40%, making it possible to accept more aircraft, aircraft of better performance or both. Another idea now being developed is the mattress deck, which makes the fitting of under carriages to jet aircraft unnecessary.

The carriers themselves belong to three main types, the largest being the Fleet carriers. These are primarily designed for use in a task force, accompanied by cruisers, and possibly a battleship with destroyers to act as a screen. The Royal Navy has six ships of this type, the *Indomitable*, *Illustrious* and *Victorious* of some 30,000 tons; the 32,000 ton *Implacable* and *Indefatigable*, all of some 30 knots. Then there is the 800 ft. long 36,800 ton *Eagle*, which joined the Home Fleet in 1952. Next there are the five 18,000 ton Light Fleet carriers of the *Glory* class, which have a speed of 24 knots, and whose purpose is to provide convoy protection against enemy submarines and aircraft. Four of these, the *Glory*, *Ocean*, *Theseus* and *Triumph* have won fame from the performance of their planes in the Korean theatre of war.

FINALLY there are the Specialist Light Fleet carriers, *Perseus* and *Unicorn*, which are designed for A/C maintenance and ferry duties, and too, the *Campania*, normally used as a ferry carrier.

Besides these, the *Ark Royal*, a sister to the *Eagle*, is now completing, while the four Improved Light Fleet carriers of the Hermes class are due to go into service in the near future. These, the *Hermes*, *Bulwark*, *Centaur* and *Albion*, are of about 23,000 tons and will have a speed of some 30 knots.

In a large carrier five main groups of aircraft are carried, each designed for its own specialised work. First there is the fighter. The Hawker Sea Fury, still in service, has proved an excellent aircraft and done first rate work as a fighter bomber in Korea, but, being piston engined, has had its day, so is being replaced by the

Only from the air can you fully appreciate the vast size of a modern aircraft carrier. Here a 'Sea Hawk' comes in to land on H.M.S. 'Eagle' the newest and largest of its type in the Royal Navy.

Vickers Supermarine Attacker, which is powered by a Rolls Royce Nene turbo-jet. This, the Navy's first jet fighter is being used as a stop gap until the new Hawker Sea Hawk comes into operation. This sleek looking, single-seater, with a Rolls Royce Nene 4 turbo-jet has a span and length of 39 feet, and is armed with 4–20 m.m. cannon. Another plane designed for this work, and now in production is the De Havilland Sea Venom (DH Ghost turbo-jet), a twin boom two-seater, all weather fighter.

Turning to the Torpedo Strike aircraft, which are de-signed for use against enemy vessels beyond the range of shore based planes, we find the present Firebrand is to be replaced by the more powerful Westland Wyvern, which is driven by an Armstrong Siddeley Python contra propeller turbine. With a length of 42 feet 3 inches, it has a span of 44 feet, and is armed with 4–20 m.m. cannon and torpedo, bombs or rockets.

The third group is the Anti-Submarine plane, which at present is represented by the Firefly 6, which as a fighter bomber has also won laurels for itself in Korea. This will shortly be superseded by the Fairey Gannet,

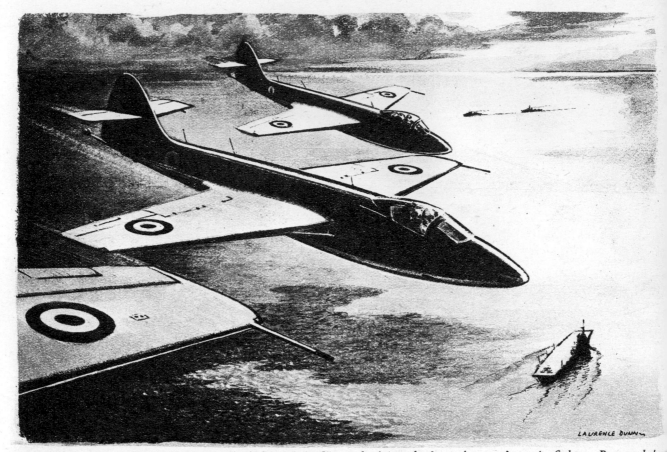

The Hawker 'Sea Hawk' now coming into service replaces the 'Attacker' as the navy's main fighter. Powered by
Rolls Royce Nene jets, it has a maximum speed of about 550 m.p.h.

a specialist 3-seater A/S plane. Driven by an Armstrong Siddeley Double Mamba twin propeller turbine, it is 43 feet in length and has a span of 54 feet 4 inches.

Coming to Helicopters we find the Dragonfly is proving invaluable for liaison and rescue duties, while larger models for A/S duties are coming along. For this work the helicopter has a very great future, as it can operate not only from carriers but also from merchant ships, the latter only needing to be fitted with a take-off platform.

Then, too, there is the special radar equipped Skyraider aircraft, which carries equipment as elaborate as that found on any ship and which by flying high over its own vessels can vastly extend their radar vision.

Every carrier has its own shore station and when in port for any length of time the various squadrons fly off, either to their own or other convenient base ashore. Each squadron is completely self-contained and on arrival retains its own entity, only needing to be provided with accommodation, food and stores.

Turning to personnel, we find that only men of commissioned rank may fly from carriers and that the great majority are ex-RNVR men. Today, besides a certain proportion drawn from the permanent service officers of the Executive branch, the intake of pilots and observers is mainly from Dartmouth entries seeking a permanent commission and from a larger group who are granted short service commissions lasting eight years, at the expiry of which many are then granted permanent commissions, or failing that a gratuity of £1,500. The Dartmouth entry is given a thorough training in all aspects of naval life before specialising as a pilot or observer, but the short service man starts with only a basic seamanship training.

One great problem is the fact that many men by the time they reach 35 or so are too stale for much flying. By being trained in seamanship the Dartmouth entry can switch over to other Naval duties and continue with normal progress and promotion. The short service entry, when granted a permanent commission, is then given this complementary training, so that he too becomes a dual purpose man. Thus, in due course, the very great majority of naval officers will be in a position to develop still more the close links which exist between the two aspects of the Navy – sea and air.

So you want to be a
SPORTS REPORTER?

One of Britain's ace sports journalists tells you about his job

Written by ROBERT FINDLAY *and illustrated by* JOHN CHAMBERLAIN

HOW does one start to become a sports reporter or editor? No two newspapermen ever begin the same way, for there is no direct route into journalism. But there are dozens of intensely interesting side tracks which lead to the same goal – your name on your article in a national newspaper.

Let's see how some of today's well-known journalists began. John Macadam, a well known sports columnist, worked in a shipyard in Greenock. One of his mates was a youth named William Cumming, and William had the bright idea one day of contributing a paragraph about something which had happened in the shipyard to the local paper, the *Greenock Telegraph*.

At the end of the month William received a postal order for his trouble and there and then decided this was a grand way of increasing one's income.

He reported every little incident he saw, and added a few character studies of the people you meet in a shipyard, and in due course his workmate John Macadam, said to himself "I must have a 'go' at this" and that was the start of his climb to Fleet Street.

William Cumming became editor of his local paper,

and developed into one of the finest journalists in all Scotland as a contributor to weekly and national newspapers on all kinds of subjects.

John Macadam widened the range of his contributions. He sent them to bigger papers in nearby Glasgow, and before long he was invited to become a junior reporter on the *Glasgow Evening Times*.

At that time, remember, he was not a sporting journalist. He was an all round journalist. He became chief sub-editor of the *Scottish Daily Express* and later, when he came to London, he wrote a sporting column for the *Sunday Dispatch*, *News Chronicle* and later the *Daily Express*.

How did I start? Well, I learned shorthand and typing and then applied for a job as a telephonist on the *Scottish Daily Express*.

I got the job which entailed taking down a reporter's story over the telephone in shorthand and transcribing it on a typewriter.

The copy would then go to the chief sub-editor who would decide what was to be done with it.

I don't think I was a very good telephonist, or telephone reporter, for they fired me after a year during an economy campaign, but it turned out well in the end for

Life at my Fleet Street desk is busy, noisy, but engrossing.

I went to the *Glasgow Weekly Herald* as a junior reporter on the strength of my experience with the *Scottish Daily Express*.

Two other boys applied for jobs on the *Daily Express* at the same time. One was named Douglas Machray. He was a form boy. He sat on a bench or form and when a sub-editor wanted something he would yell "Boy" and Machray would nip smartly over to the sub-editor and perform whatever was the task on hand – generally taking a finished story to the printer, getting tea or fetching something from the library.

In due course Machray, showing promise, was allowed to help the sub-editors, and in a couple of years he was a junior sub-editor, handling everything from City or financial copy to crime and politics.

Now he is an executive on one national newspaper while the other form boy, Edward Fenton, ranks high in his profession on another.

But the boys from little villages and small towns have just as much chance as those in bigger places. John Batson, who became Gilroy of the *Sunday Graphic*, started on the *North Eastern Echo*.

He wrote a letter to the editor asking for a job, and got one – as an assistant to a district reporter in some unsung and unexciting corner of Northumberland.

There he learned his craft, interviewing, writing, news-gathering, how to smell out news etc. He worked long hours, but eventually he was promoted from district work to the head office and from there to the *Manchester Daily Express*, and then Fleet Street was a small jump.

I said John Batson wrote a letter. Ah, that's where so many budding journalists fall down. Ask one hundred boys to write a letter and ninety-nine will start "Dear Sir, I beg to apply for the position of junior reporter on your newspaper. I am etc etc".

The editor is not interested in the ninety-nine. A journalist must have initiative and character in his writing even in a letter, and the boy who gets right off the beaten track in his letter will have more notice taken of him.

Your letter should reveal the journalist in you. It might begin "Dear Sir, I want to be a journalist. I want to be one because I know I can be a good one" – and so on. Strike an original note.

If you are a London boy you should apply to your local paper. You might find it easier to get a job as a messenger on a Fleet Street paper, but such jobs seldom lead to editorial jobs. Fleet Street has no time to train youngsters. You must get your training on a local or provincial newspaper.

It's hard work, mind you. As a junior reporter you

might work 12 or 16 hours a day for about £2 a week. Your friends, perhaps technicians or clerks, will be earning much more than you at the start, but you will soon pass them when you learn your craft and in the end your earnings will surpass theirs.

The London Union minimum for a newspaperman is £14 a week, but, depending on your ability, you can earn up to £5000 a year, and there are more good jobs around the £1500 mark in journalism than in most professions.

So my advice to you is: Start learning shorthand and typing. Whenever you see a street incident, or hear of some local event, write it out and send it in to your local paper, making sure your name and address is on top of your copy.

You may or may not get paid for it, but you will be making yourself known and showing your initiative.

There are stories everywhere – in every building, street, person and place. The imaginative mind finds them.

You need not wait until you've learned your shorthand and typing before applying for a job. You can be a junior reporter while learning.

If you don't know where to apply, go to your local library and ask for Willings Press Guide. In it you will find the name and address of every newspaper in Britain.

Of course, a really smart lad might go right up to a newspaper office and ask to see the editor without writing. He may be turned away, but often such an approach bears fruit if the editor is impressed with the lad's keenness and appearance.

I have indicated what is known as "the hard way" into journalism. There is another way, just as hard – but what I might call the scholastic way.

A youth takes his General Certificate, then goes to a University to take whatever degree or study whatever subjects interest him, and if he has journalism at the back of his mind, he will be interested in subjects bearing on literature, history and such classical subjects.

Eventually, his University education completed, he may, either by direct application or through influence, persuade a newspaper to try him out as a reporter, a feature writer or even as a leader writer. A 'leader' is the Opinion column of a newspaper and reflects the policy of the paper.

Many fine journalists come from the Universities. Some use journalism as a training for politics, like Tom Driberg M.P. and J. Mallalieu M.P., both Fleet Street men. But the local papers produce a hundred journalists for every one produced by the Universities.

It is important to remember that, however keen you are on ending up a Sports reporter, you have got to

"Robert Findlay will now say a few words."

learn your craft in a general way first and it may well be that the experience you gain in your early years in journalism will lead you to change your preference for sport. In the meantime you will have had many opportunities to indulge your love of sport. It's just as much fun covering a village cricket match as a Test Match. Indeed, the young reporter at the village match is probably given a bigger welcome than the ace reporter from a National newspaper who covers the Test Match.

I remember the glow of pride I felt on covering my first amateur Soccer match. The hospitality enchanted me – a special seat, a programme, a cup of tea at half-time and an invitation to attend the club dinner in the evening.

I had a shock at the dinner, though. There were about two hundred people present, and suddenly the chairman announced, without previously warning me, that "Robert Findlay will now say a few words about the Press."

A newspaper man is always being confronted by the unexpected so he must be quick-witted. In this case there was nothing for it but to speak so I started off with a story which I had kept just for such an occasion.

It was about a Christian being thrown to the lions. As each hungry, snarling lion bounded up to the young man, he whispered in its ear and it slunk away as if cowed.

Eventually, the people gave the "Thumbs Up" sign and Nero ordered the young Christian to be released. "But tell me," said Nero, "what is your power over the beasts ? What magic words did you whisper in the lions' ears ?"

"Oh" replied the young man, "I merely said to each lion 'you'll be expected to say a few words after lunch'."

Fight reporting is one of the most exciting events to cover. Individual combat, the primeval war of one man against another, the smell of resin, the clash of sweating, struggling bodies, the flash of fists and the roar of spectators all combine to inject fight reporting with colour and drama.

Reputations stand and fall on boxing reports. I remember the wife of a well known boxer asking him on arriving home if he had won.

"Yes" he replied. "And did you have a good fight ?" inquired the anxious wife.

"Oh" said the boxer, "I won't know that till I see the papers in the morning."

The young sports reporter may be called to cover all sports, but on the big daily newspapers one man generally is responsible for one, two or three sports.

Thus, a man might cover Cricket in the summer and Rugby in the winter; or Boxing and Soccer in the winter and Athletics in the summer. Or he might go on a winter tour, say with the M.C.C. to Australia, and return to cover County Cricket in the summer.

Sometimes the sporting journalist acts as a "ghost" for some famous sportsman who knows the game but can't write it.

The "ghost" will chat with the celebrity, get his ideas on some aspect of his sport, and then write it for him. The celebrity's name, of course, goes on the story – not the journalist's – though in some cases the journalist deserves rather more credit!

There is a story of a former England cricketer who was employed to write articles on Test matches with the aid of a "ghost".

Each night the "ghost" would seek out the cricketer and ask him what he thought of the day's play. The reply would follow similar lines each night. "Jolly good play (or bad as the case may be) old man. Just put that in your own words."

The result would be a column of Test Cricket in the paper next day!

A friend of mine, Michael Ryan, wrote Jack Doyle's reminiscences for a Sunday newspaper. He would have a chat with Doyle whenever he could pin down that volatile character, and that was all Doyle knew about the story until he read the paper on Sunday morning.

On a Sunday morning Doyle would read the latest instalment, throw out his chest, and remark to the company in his rich Irish brogue: "Shure, but I'm in great writing form this marning."

In conclusion it is interesting to remember that Maureen Connolly – Little Mo – is training to be a sports reporter. But though she won the Wimbledon women's championship at 17 she still had to start the hard way of running errands and doing very humble jobs for her paper in America. One can play a game brilliantly without being able to write about it well, and in the case of Little Mo she started to learn her trade of reporter from the ground level – the way *you* should learn it.

SOLUTION TO PICTURE QUIZ ON PAGE 131

1. Javelin.   2. Blackbird.   3. Bloodhound.   4. Perch.   5. Cheetah.   6. Merchant Navy.

UNCLE: "What position are you in at school, Derek ?"
DEREK: "Centre-forward in soccer, Uncle, right back in lessons!"

Fun with an ant house

Written by Frank Jordan. Illustrated by Norman Satchel

SOME time ago I sat idly watching the movements of some ants outside a nest beside a tiny stream. They seemed greatly excited over something, and after a few minutes I discovered the reason. Apparently some of them wanted to cross to the other side but, disliking water (though they must have dampness), and never having learned to be sailors, they selected a tall grass stem. This, hundreds of the little engineers climbed until by weight of numbers the stem slowly began to arch across the rivulet.

Other ants followed and eventually the top end of the stalk touched the other bank. Some of the workers landed, and cemented the stem to the ground with damp clay to form a bridge. After that the whole colony marched over it to the other bank.

This fascinating feat of patient antine engineering held me to the spot for the better part of the day, and by the time the labourers had all crossed the stream I was feeling pretty hungry. So it was not until early the next morning that I returned to the rivulet, to find the old nest still heaving with life.

What had probably happened was that the colony had divided, the rebels taking their own new queen to found another community somewhere else. But why the adventurers had chosen the difficult route across the little river, instead of some other place on the same side, was a mystery. So was their complete disappearance. For hours I searched for signs of a new home in the making on the opposite bank, but not a trace could I find.

At this point I remembered having read of a colony of another kind of ant which had crossed a river, too wide for an overhead bridge, by tunnelling underneath it. And from the termite story which I will tell later on, it will be clear that tunnelling, even on this scale, can be a minor operation for this most dangerous, destructive of all the ants.

It was not long after this river-bridging episode that I made friends with a man who, with his children, had built and were running an ant house of their own. It would be difficult to find another pastime quite so fascinating. You can buy a ready-made observation nest, but it is much more fun to make one yourself, and it can be done quite cheaply.

The model made by my friend consisted of two sheets of glass measuring one by $1\frac{1}{2}$ feet, laid flat and held about an inch apart by strips of slightly thicker glass on three sides. The result was a kind of ant sandwich, the edges being bound together by adhesive tape, with which the fourth side, or door, was also sealed. The nest was then half-filled with very light soil, or sand, and laid flat on a table, the legs of which were set in cups or pans of water, to keep the ants at home.

Having made this simple ant house, you would next dig up a real nest. The best tool for this is a scoop or shovel-spade. Dig it into the ground below the ant-hill, then tip the load quickly into a closely-weaved sack or bag, so that your prisoners cannot escape through the sides. Then tie the sack's mouth tightly with several

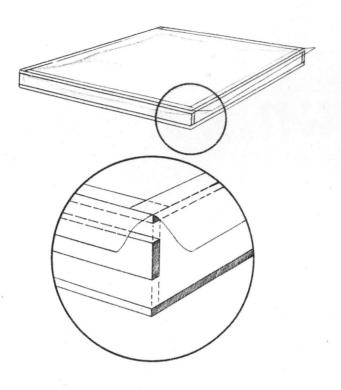

Here we show you how to bind the edges of your ant 'sandwich' with adhesive tape.

loops of string for the same reason. It is, of course, vital to include the queen; and with luck she will now be inside the sack. But in case she is not, you should go on lightly turning over the soil with your shovel to look for her. But do not prolong this operation, or hundreds of the enraged ants will be running up your legs.

You will know her majesty by her large size and her great popularity, for she will be surrounded by attendant winged drones, or males.

A generous share of these should also be included in your capture, as well as plenty of pupae, or children, which are distinguishable from eggs, these being tiny rice-like specks, while the pupae are living larvae.

Now carry the sack to the table, quickly but gently empty it of earth and ants, leave the sack, with its strays, open on one corner, and spread the nest thinly on the table with a trowel, so that the sand will dry fairly quickly.

For a while the small fry will fuss about angrily, but will in time cool down. So will the left-behinds in the sack, and all will head for the slightly damped artificial nest, over which you will have spread a black cloth to screen it from the light.

Ants will die in dry earth; they also dislike bright light, especially sunlight, so the cloth should always be kept in place except while you are actually spying on the colony. Should you wish to transfer the nest to another place, you must of course seal up the door during the move. Now the aim and routine of ant life unfolds before you, and you discover that the normal activities of an ant palace are first-class entertainment.

You can watch the building of streets, the excavation of tunnels and store-rooms. You can spy on the construction of a royal chamber for the queen, and day and night nurseries for the children, who are tended with infinite care.

Keep the house stocked with dead beetles, small earthworms, flies, meat scraps. Provide occasional treats of sugar or sweets, which they love, and keep the soil slightly damp by leaving inside a well-moistened piece of sponge, which you should recharge at intervals.

Many kinds of ants keep "cows"; these are aphis or green-flies which are found on rose bushes or other juicy plants. So, occasionally pick a fly-covered stem and give it to the ants. You will probably find that they will lead their cows out to pasture on weeds every day, if you let them. And through a magnifying glass you can watch workers milking the cows, which they do by softly stroking the green bodies to squeeze out drops of the sweet fluid which the flies secrete, as a real cow secretes milk.

Raids by gangster ants and racketeer beetles add to the excitement of the ant city. But, as your water-cups insulate the city from the outside world, you will have to introduce the raiders yourself, if you wish this additional activity, which is of course normal to a natural ant house.

However, be careful not to bring in too many, otherwise the invaders may prove too much for the soldier ants, and obstruct the work of the colony. After a battle with intruders, the wounded are tended by nurses. Observe, too, how clean the ants keep their quarters, removing refuse from the streets and nurseries, tipping it into sanitary "tanks", then replacing the spent sand with clean sand from outside the nest. All life revolves round the queen and her thousands of children.

It is, of course, possible that your parents will be a little doubtful about your ant-house adventures. To reassure them you could keep the table in an outhouse. In any case, this would be the best place. But there is really little likelihood that your ants will escape from the table if you are careful to keep the bowls always filled with water.

After a while, you can carry out a few experiments. Pull up another table, and join the two with a cardboard bridge. On the second table put a dab of honey, or a number of eggs from the nest. With a twig pick up the first ant who ventures out and drop her on the decoy.

Spread a dark cloth over your ant house to screen it from the light.

While she is investigating, dab a speck of white paint on her back, so that you will be able to follow her movements.

After a while she will rush off home and bring out some of her sisters. Soon a stream of workers will be heading for the prize. You can form up other tables with connecting bridges, each table having its individual decoy. When the columns of foragers have carried home their tiny loads of honey or eggs, and the prize is finished, the last of the adventurers will return home, and you can then remove the additional tables, once more isolating your ant palace from the rest of the world.

You could also test the theory that ants determine their direction by the sun. To do this, take an ant from the nest in the morning, shut it in a pill-box (allowing

an inlet of air) on the corner of the table until the afternoon, then let it out. It will have been so deceived by the altered direction of the sun's rays, that it will take a long time to find its way home. On the other hand, imprison the ant in the same way for a few minutes only, and the captive will probably head straight for home without having to scout for the proper route.

Other experiments will occur to you as time goes on, but remember always to work them out yourself beforehand, so that you can be certain that the ants which are the subject of your tests will eventually take *themselves* home. Otherwise you may have to get them back yourself, and this can be a difficult business, if they have other ideas.

Attendance on your ant house is sure to rouse interest in other ants and their nests. It is found that queens, drones or reproductives, soldiers, and workers all come from eggs which, to begin with, are identical. They take on their differences through variations in the type and quantity of food supplied to the eggs. And those which become workers, which alone forage for food, receive from the queen a chemical scent which conditions them to the smell of their own colony, and encourages them to return to it.

The queen presides over her realm with the rigid sternness of the ruler of a totalitarian state, which indeed it is. Yet she finds time to enlarge it at the prodigious rate of 50,000 to 100,000 eggs every twenty-four hours.

In the world of the ant the individual is lost in the communal despotism, leading an unattractive existence of endless hard work, unpaid and without let-up, except to sleep. So, each contributes its share to the rich collective life of the whole colony. There are no strikes against the inflexible will and direction of the queen-mother. It sounds rather like slave-driving, and you might think that it would make better sense if one species of ant were to capture thousands of a less clever species, and make slaves of them, so that the conquerors could enjoy a life of ease.

But ants are much cleverer than that. Slave-making species are rare, probably because this practice would eventually spell their own doom. One breed only is known to keep other ants as slaves. But sometimes these yellow serfs revolt against their black masters.

A pitched battle follows, from which the yellows often emerge as victors. They then make off, and found a colony of their own. But the idle and good-for-nothing blacks, left to themselves, starve to death because they have lived only to be waited on.

The rest of the world of ants is made up of species with varying tastes as to territory and diet – red ants which eat up garden plants; tree ants that make long treks from the ground to the tasty shoots at the ends of slender branches; tiny brown-black fellows which one finds almost everywhere. There are said to be altogether 4,500 separate kinds of ant. But so many of these have habits which are similar, that most of them do not belong to this article. One that certainly does is the white ant, or termite.

Three times within two years white ants have attacked parts of the Vatican buildings in Rome, and you can form an accurate idea how thoroughly these pygmy robots work, from the fact that large parts of the Vatican library, solid oak beams, and sturdy walls have succumbed to these assaults. Termites will, in a day or less, hollow out the legs of a large table, cunningly leaving a thin external shell to camouflage the destruction.

Vatican authorities have since made preparations which they hope will keep permanently at bay the cleverest, most methodically destructive of all the ants. But termites are normally a tropical species.

In Africa they reach unbelievable numbers, and can become a serious plague if not curbed. The present white-ant population of the Transvaal State alone has risen to an estimated 2,000 millions. Massed assaults on the wooden flooring and ceiling rafters of houses and public buildings reduce the Vatican invasion to the level of a minor operation by comparison.

The marauders live in vast, cleverly-built nests in the neighbourhood. Their underground galleries are often seventy feet below the artificial mounds which the ants build to serve as ventilating shafts, in case heavy rain or floods should close up their customary ground-level entrances. Once, a French entomologist, having gassed

the inmates, set himself the tremendous task of counting the populations of five adjoining termite nests. The smallest mustered nearly 20,000, the largest 94,000, though there was no way of estimating how many ants escaped the census by a timely exit, or through absence on business.

Sallies from the African nests are often difficult to trace without special aids, for ants do not always travel to and from the assault across open country; often they cannily build covered ways to screen their movements. So the Transvaal's health authorities formed anti-ant companies, equipped with flame-throwers, carbon monoxide and other poison gases. Within two weeks the ant fighters accounted for about five hundred nests and forty-five colonies. Fifteen hundred other South African health-inspectors, who any day may have to tackle a similar problem, are closely watching both methods and effects.

For the Transvaal pest-slayers are making some astonishing discoveries. For instance, painstakingly spooning out earth parallel to one marauding column which was operating along a tunnel deep beneath the floor of a house, the hunters tracked the ants to a colony on the other side of the street. Rather than attack openly the ants had burrowed thirty feet beneath a thickly-paved road to reach their objective in secret. Few obstacles seem too formidable for a termite colony bent on reaching an object which scouts have reported on as desirable. In this case the target was a house's larder, woodwork, clothes and books.

Distressing news has come from the Gold Coast, where thousands of simple native folk have been making good money as cocoa-pickers. Despite education, many of them still distrust banks, and prefer to put the bulk of their earnings in leather bags, which they bury beneath their huts, or under trees in their yam plots. Probably millions of pounds have been hidden in this way; and recently a native, digging for his savings, found that they had all disappeared, leaving behind only the sad proofs that the thieves were termites who had fancied the buried treasure – £1 notes, bags, and all – for a picnic.

Australia is also plagued with termites. On some islands off the coast houses are being built on stilts in an experimental effort to keep living-quarters free of the pests. In Darwin some houses stand on concrete piles for the same reason. But even these are being eaten through by the hungry creatures to reach the wood above.

There are also varieties of larger, vicious nomad ants which carry their queens and drones and young along with them wherever they feel the urge to go. The

Workers milk their 'cows' by softly stroking their green bodies.

Bridging a tiny rivulet by a grass stem was a fascinating feat of antine engineering.

driver ants of South America belong to this family. They are well named, for they travel in such strength that they sweep everything before them.

No creature dares to stand in the path of any army of driver ants on the move; a column may measure a hundred yards long by fifteen yards wide. As locusts lay bare agricultural land, these soldier ants sweep native villages – hastily evacuated by their inhabitants – clean of every eatable thing.

These driver excursions do, however, serve one useful purpose. Once, a daring naturalist, having received word that a horde of drivers was advancing, stood fast in a native hut to see the "fun". But first he took the precaution to stand each leg of a table in a bucket of water. Then he stood on the top and watched the invaders swarm into the hut and spread themselves over floor, walls, and ceiling. But they also hunted in every hole and crack for rats and other vermin, which they stung to death, dragged forth, and ate.

Charles Darwin called the ant "the most marvellous atom in the world, next to the human brain." It is also an interesting and important fact that the ant appears to have come to the end of its development. Ants have been found in amber, which was at least twenty million years old, and with every detail of their structure splendidly preserved. But these ants differed not at all from the ants of today.

Why ant progress has been halted is probably because, like all insects, it is limited in size. There are, in fact, Australian "bull-dog ants" – about $1\frac{1}{2}$ inches long and the world has knowledge of larger ones, but fortunately the biggest are no larger than common mice. It long seems to have been Nature's plan, in each group with which she is dealing, to develop brain at the expense of physical bulk. Thus, within each species, the larger the creature's body the lower its intelligence.

The bigger ants, though awesome because of their size, are in fact the least to be feared, since they have a lower mentality, are inferior planners, and breed in smaller numbers. If, by some unfortunate change of plan, Nature had allowed ants to develop to the stature of, say, fox terriers, and at the same time to retain the mentality of the smaller ants, it is probable that they would have prevented the existence, in the same world, of man and every other hostile animal.

All of which, you will agree, adds to the interest to be had from watching the harmless, yet highly intelligent goings-on in our home-made ant house!

● A NOVEL TRAINING SUGGESTION BY BILLY WRIGHT

You can be your own coach

● ILLUSTRATED BY S. DRIGIN

OVER two hundred lads sat tightly packed together in a Youth Club in the Midlands. As I talked football with them they sat quietly digesting every remark made and when the subject turned to coaching I felt, almost at once, that I was going to be smothered with questions.

And I was right. After in detail describing the value of young players taking an interest in this aspect of the game, it was to find dozens of lads bursting to say all together: "We never see a coach. Is there a way out of this difficulty ?"

My answer seemed to shock them.

"Why not try helping yourselves ?" I asked. "Why not try *coaching* yourselves ?"

For some seconds there was a silence. Somehow I've a hunch the lads thought I had taken leave of my senses, but when we settled down once more to talk about my "Coach Yourself" scheme they quickly became enthusiastic supporters of a movement which I know is every week growing.

Well, what are the basic requirements if you want to help yourself improve the standard of your football ? Firstly, of course, a football. Then a garden wall – providing your father or the man next door is informed of your intentions! – and a few long sticks; even better some cricket stumps. Then, these essentials at your disposal, you can commence work.

The first thing you should do is chalk up on the garden wall a goal, then break this up into eight squares. This task completed, mark each square with a number and you are ready for 'target practice'. From varying distances, and angles, try and place the ball into a numbered square chosen by you. "That's easy," you say. Try it and be amazed just how difficult it can become. This form of target practice, I might add, was one I practised for years as a schoolboy. As a matter of fact when first I joined Wolverhampton Wanderers, and worked on the ground-staff, I used to spend part of my lunch hour hitting a ball at a similar target. Believe me, too, it was years before I could really take aim and in my heart know that I was going to score a 'bull'.

This type of shooting practice can be useful in another way. It is, I contend, one of the best methods of learning to keep the ball low. Never forget the most difficult shot a goalkeeper ever has to face is one which keeps low, a few inches from the turf, and to acquire an ability to shoot low and accurately demands constant practice. What I used to do was draw a thick chalk line about eighteen inches from the ground and then, re-membering always to get my body *OVER* the ball, try to shoot it inside the line.

No, I did not quickly master the art. More often than not I either hit the chalk mark, or finished just above it, but I never gave up trying. In the end I felt pleased to report to my schoolmaster I could perform the trick six times out of ten.

My old friend the garden wall has often come in use-ful for helping me pass a ball quickly and take a return pass in my stride. Firstly, with the ball at my feet, I would run with the ball on my left hand and imagine I was at outside right. I would hit the ball with the out-side of my left foot and have to run forward quickly as it rebounded to me as if my inside-right had sent out a return pass.

I did the same thing with the wall on my right, assuming I was a left-winger, and the outcome was I found myself acquiring 'balance'. It did not matter from which direction the ball came to me, or at what height or speed, I was able to either take it in my stride or trap it with ease.

Try this yourself. It really is a form of practice you'll find helps perfect your game.

Tired of practising at the wall ? Right, let's borrow a few sticks from mother's store of firewood, or, as I said earlier, get out your cricket stumps. Then, on the lawn – or in a field – peg out the sticks or stumps about five yards apart, and then commence, slowly at first, but gradually working up a faster tempo, to dribble the ball between them. I've always thought this good fun, apart from good practice, and you will be surprised, if you stick at this practice, just how quickly your ball control will improve, and how you are also able to master your own body; a very important thing.

Now for a spot of heading practice. To commence with, before you ever start trying to head a ball cor-rectly I think it essential you should be able to 'climb' high into the air. "And how does one learn to do this ?" I can already hear many of you asking. It's quite easy.

Practise hitting the ball hard with your forehead, straight ahead at an imaginary goal.

Whenever possible, as you are walking to school, or work, try suddenly leaping into the air.

Maybe you'll find some people looking at you with mingled surprise and pity, but ignore them. Get on with your 'high jump' practice and set your sights upon becoming as good a "leaper" as the one and only Tommy Lawton.

"What happens next ?" you ask.

More practice.

Have you a tree in the garden, or better still a beam in a barn ? You have ? Good! Your next task is to tie a long piece of thick string to the lace of the ball and then suspend the ball at varying heights either from the bow of a tree or a beam. Then you can really get to work

Dribble the ball between the stumps, slowly at first but gradually increase speed.

I think we'll now return to our old friend the garden wall for some more practice, this time to strengthen our weak foot. No, do not wear boots on both feet, but just one boot on your weak foot. On the other place a slipper. Then, for up to half-an-hour, hit the ball with your "weak" foot against the wall.

At first you're going to find it monotonous, but, as the foot begins to feel stronger, you'll get quite a kick out of your success – and I'm not trying to be "punny". This, I shall always contend, is the only method of strengthening a "swinger" and becoming a real double-footed footballer.

"But why the slipper on one foot ?" asked one lad.

The answer's a simple one. You'll automatically find yourself kicking the ball with the foot wearing a *boot*.

This practice can also be used for helping you improve your trapping ability, for after slamming the ball at the wall with your "swinger", afterwards try and trap it correctly as it rebounds towards you at varying heights and speeds. Again, please do not be disappointed if at first you find the going hard. It takes time, and patience, to really learn to "tame" a ball correctly.

Our old friend the garden wall is also useful for learning to place a ball accurately with your head. Throw the ball hard against the wall and as it rebounds towards you pick out the exact spot where you wish to put it. I'd suggest you take up a position near the goal you've chalked up on the wall and try to aim into one of the squares you'd numbered for your shooting practice.

Once more I must stress to all you young fellows that on no account can you afford to be disappointed if at first you flop. Keep on trying. Never quit.

In the end, although the journey may seem a long one, you'll acquire a football technique and ability which will be the envy of your pals.

learning to nod the ball correctly with your forehead. As you leap try flicking the ball first from left to right. Practise hitting it hard with your forehead, straight ahead at an imaginary goal, as if you really hated that ball. There's no half-measures, I must stress, about heading a football. You either put everything behind your nod or else you flop and probably end up with a very bad headache.

Give this heading practice a trial. You'll be amazed how quickly you will improve.

CHICKO . . .   BY THELWELL

ANSWERS TO PUZZLE CORNER ON PAGE 154

1. WEIGHTS

1 lb., 3 lb., 9 lb.

2. SIX VOWELS

1. Facetiously; 2. Abstemiously.

3. ACCOUNT RENDERED

One coin must not be a shilling, because it is a penny. The other is a shilling.

4. FIVE FAMOUS ENGLISHMEN

1. Nelson; 2. Cromwell; 3. Churchill; 4. Shakespeare; 5. Marlborough.

5. JACK AND JILL

Bill. He takes only two minutes longer to run six miles than Jack takes to run five.

6. ANISEED

Carboy.

7. WORD SQUARE

¹T	²I	³D	⁴E	⁵S
⁶I	N	A	N	E
⁷D	A	N	T	E
⁸E	N	T	E	R
⁹S	E	E	R	S

8. SUBSCRIPTION

Eleven.

9. THOUGHT FOR TODAY

"Evil rats on no star live."

10. JOSEPH AND JOSEPHINE

The little girl is Josephine's daughter.

11. BUGGINS

Buggins does better for himself if he chooses the second alternative. If you don't believe me, work it out for yourself.

12. PENTACLE

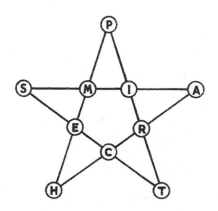

PRINTED BY ERIC BEMROSE LTD., LONG LANE, LIVERPOOL, 9